Kathy Schrock's
Every Day of the School Year Series

The American Memory Collection

from A-Z

Primary Resource Guide and Reproducible
Activities Across the Curriculum

Grades 4-6

by Gail Petri

LINWORTH LEARNING

From the Minds of Teachers

Linworth Publishing, Inc.
Worthington, Ohio

Editor: Cindy Barden

Design and Production: Good Neighbor Press, Inc., Grand Junction, CO 81503

Published by Linworth Publishing, Inc.
480 East Wilson Bridge Road, Suite L
Worthington, Ohio 43085

ISBN: 1-58683-117-8

5 4 3

A Word From Kathy Schrock:

Welcome to the *Every Day of the School Year Series!* As an educator, library media specialist, and now technology administrator, I know how important it is for the classroom teacher to extend the learning experiences in the classroom. With the current focus on standards-based teaching, learning, and assessment, I felt it was important to supply classroom teachers and library media specialists with activities which directly support the curriculum, but, at the same time, allow for creative teachers to provide supplementary and extension activities for their students.

The activities in this series are varied in scope, but all of them provide practical tips, tricks, ideas, activities and units. Many of the activities include related print and Internet sites which are easily collected by the classroom teacher before engaging in the activity. There are handouts, worksheets, and much more throughout the books, too.

In my job as technology administrator for a school district, I am often able to plan lessons with teachers and visit classrooms to observe the teaching of the lesson. In addition, as the creator and maintainer, since 1995, of Kathy Schrock's Guide for Educators (http://discoveryschool.com/schrockguide/), a portal of categorized Web sites for teachers, I often receive e-mail from teachers who are searching for practical, creative, and easy-to-implement activities for the classroom. I hope this series provides just the impetus for you to stretch and enhance your textbook, lesson, and standards-based unit by use of these activities!

If you have any titles you would like to see added to the series, or would like to author yourself, drop me a note at kathy@kathyschrock.net

Acknowledgements

Thank you to the many teachers, librarians, students, and family members whose time, ideas, and encouragement have helped make this book a reality.

Leni Donlan, Library of Congress Learning Page Project Coordinator, has been my mentor and true friend throughout the process. She provided answers, advice, people contacts, and a wonderful sense of humor during my many hours of research and writing. I couldn't have completed this book without her!

Without Doris Waud, Fyle Elementary School fifth grade teacher, valued colleague, and Library of Congress American Memory Fellow partner, I might never have begun the exciting discovery of the American Memory riches. Her creative ideas, enthusiasm for trying new things, and willingness to help whenever needed are what make Doris so special! Collaborating with Doris has been a highlight of my teaching career.

Extra thanks to Library Media Specialist Mary Alice Anderson of Winona, Minnesota for her lesson contributions and continued support throughout the project. Getting to know Mary Alice has been a bonus!

Last, but not least, special thanks to Kathy Schrock for inviting me to write this book and having the confidence and patience to stick with me until I finished! Her expertise, insights, and advice have been invaluable.

Most importantly—thank you to the Library of Congress for making the American Memory digital collections available to the public! How lucky we are to have such a wonderful national treasure to share!

Table of Contents

Table of Contents *Continued*

Explore the World's Largest Library

Explore the Library of Congress, the largest library in the world, located in Washington, D.C. Developed and maintained for the citizens of the United States of America, the Library of Congress is available online.

You can search its catalogs, visit online exhibitions, obtain legislative information, explore kid-friendly resources, and best of all, discover America's history through primary resources in the American Memory collection.

http://www.loc.gov/

Stereoscopic View of the Library of Congress 1902

1.3

From the Library of Congress (LOC) homepage you can:

★ Link to the American Memory collection
★ Link to Thomas for Legislative Information
★ Check out the International Horizons Gateway to the World
★ Visit America's Library
★ Explore the Online Exhibitions and Galleries
★ Search the LOC Catalogs
★ Check out the Research Centers
★ Find out what happened Today in History
★ Link to the Teachers' Learning Page
★ Read about LOC News and Events
★ Link to Self-Serve Workshops
★ Access the Learning Page/Educators/Handouts

The **American Memory Collection**

Imagine having all the primary sources you could ever want right at your fingertips! Log on to find millions of primary sources at the Library of Congress American Memory website which includes over 100 collections of digitized documents, photographs, recordings, moving pictures, and text from the Library's Americana collections. To explore the collections go to:

http://memory.loc.gov/

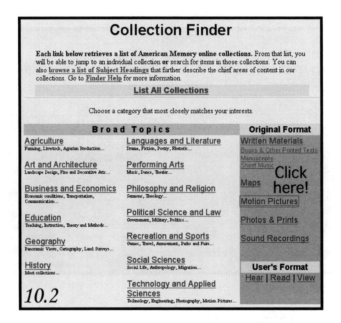

From the American Memory homepage you can:

- ★ Go to the Collection Finder to learn about the collections
- ★ Go to the Search page to search for a topic
- ★ Go to Today in History
- ★ Find out What's New to the collection
- ★ Learn about Copyright and Restrictions
- ★ Get Technical Information
- ★ Learn about Future Collections
- ★ Connect to a Featured Collection
- ★ View a Search Example of the Day

Visit the Learning Page

Created especially for educators, the LOC Learning Page helps you get started using primary resources. Tap into its ready-to-use features, activities, lesson plans, professional development opportunities, and more to help integrate the American Memory resources into your everyday teaching.

http://memory.loc.gov/ammem/ndlpedu/

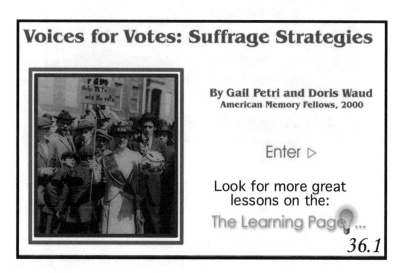

From the Learning Page you can:

★ Learn how to get started using the collection
★ Access ready-to-use lesson plans
★ Link to Features and Activities
★ Find Collection Connections for your curriculum
★ Join the Community Center to see how other teachers are using the collection
★ Access Professional Development opportunities
★ Explore What is New on the Learning Page

Using Primary Sources

16.2

Primary resources are available in many formats. They include images, documents, media files, or objects. They may be hundreds of years old or brand new. They come from varied sources that offer different points of view.

Primary sources are important because they provide original, firsthand information about historical and current events. Using primary sources exposes students to multiple perspectives of events and issues.

Studying primary sources encourages students to ask questions, gives them practice in thinking critically, and enhances their sense of historical understanding.

Primary resources can be integrated across the curriculum in hundreds of creative and fun ways to excite your students and positively affect learning.

Today's technological advances have made primary sources easily available online. The Library of Congress American Memory Collection is an amazing online resource for primary source materials related to the history and culture of the United States. With over seven million items from over 100 historical collections, this wonderful resource can be a bit overwhelming at first.

The activities in this book are designed to introduce you and your students to the wonders of the American Memory collection. Legal information about the use of the items can be found at:

http://memory.loc.gov/ammem/amdisc.html

and

http//memory.loc.gov/learn/resources/cpyrt/index.html

Using This Book

Topics in this book are organized alphabetically by title. Each topic includes multiple activities. Most topics include one or more reproducible activities.

Activities can be completed by individual students or in a group setting. They can be used alone or combined to create a more extensive unit. Each topic focuses on using primary sources from one or more of the American Memory collection.

Sometimes site addresses change. If you have trouble locating a site listed in this book, go to the LOC homepage (**http://loc.gov**). Type in the title of the collection or name of the site. This will often lead you directly to the site.

It would be helpful to bookmark or save the sites as "Favorites" in advance to make it easier for students to find the specific sites they need to complete the activities.

Detailed instructions about creating American Memory bookmarks can be found at:

http://memory.loc.gov/learn/resources/tech/link.html

Many primary resource formats are highlighted within the activities and most activities can be adapted to meet the skill levels of your students.

Knowing how to analyze a primary source is an important skill. Graphic organizers help students become proficient in this process. Students can use the Primary Resource Companion on page 6 to collect information and organize their ideas.

The questioning strategy—using who, what, where, when, and why questions—can also be helpful when examining primary resources. Students can use the graphic organizer and list of sample questions on pages 7 and 8 for this purpose.

The Table of Contents lists both the titles of the teaching pages and the reproducible activities.

The Index lists more specific subject topics.

Name _____ Date _____

Primary Resource Companion

What type of primary resource is this?	What details can you locate when you study this primary resource?
(Check one.)	

What type of primary resource is this?
(Check one.)

- ☐ Advertisement
- ☐ Cartoon
- ☐ Map
- ☐ Motion Picture
- ☐ Photograph
- ☐ Poster
- ☐ Sound Recording
- ☐ Document
- ☐ Other:

_____

What details can you locate when you study this primary resource?

★ What is the title (caption) of the primary resource?

★ Where (in which American Memory collection) did you find the primary resource?

★ Who is the author or creator of the primary resource (if available)?

★ When was the primary resource created (if available)?

What do you actually SEE, HEAR, or READ when you study this resource?

What do you think you KNOW about this resource?

What QUESTIONS do you have about this resource?

Where might you look for ANSWERS to your questions?

Question Organizer

Title of Primary Resource: _____

American Memory Collection: _____

WHO?	**WHAT?**
WHEN?	**WHERE?**
WHY?	**HOW?**

Sample Questions for Primary Resource Analysis

Who?

Who created this resource (author, photographer, etc.)?
Who do you think is the intended audience for this resource?
Who do you actually see pictured in this resource?
Who are you listening to in the audio resource?
Who are the major historical people referred to in this resource?

What?

What is the format of this resource (photo, map, etc.)?
What was the purpose of this resource?
What was the creator's point of view?
What can you learn about life in the United States when you study this resource?
What do you see or hear as you study this resource?
What would it be like to live in the time or place this resource was created?
What questions does this primary resource raise?

When?

When was this resource created?
When is the historical time period of this resource?
When this resource was created, what else was happening in the United States?

Where?

Where was this resource created?
Where is the geographical setting of this resource?
Where is this resource located in the Library of Congress collections?

Why?

Why was this document created?
Why did you choose this resource to study?
Why are the people in the photo doing what they are doing?
Why is this resource important in history?

How?

How can this resource help historical researchers today?
How do you feel when you read, view, or listen to this resource?
How can you learn more about this resource?

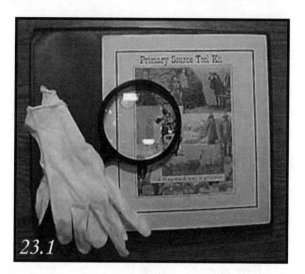

23.1

These group activities introduce students to the website and help them learn strategies to locate and analyze documents in the American Memory collection.

Activities:

★ **American Memory Gallery Sampler**

Explore this sampler for an overview of the varied types of documents, photographs, maps, sound files, and movies available in the American Memory collection. You may wish to download this PDF file for personal reference and/or as a resource for students.

http://lcweb2.loc.gov/ammem/ndlpedu/educators/workshop/search/gallery.html

★ **How Do I Find It?**

Use this site to help students develop successful strategies for searching the American Memory collection.

http://lcweb2.loc.gov/ammem/ndlpedu/educators/workshop/discover/find.html

Click on the highlighted options at this site:

★ **Pictures as Primary Sources**

This activity helps students gather ideas for using a camera to create modern day primary sources.

★ **Primary Source Toolkit**

Follow the instructions to create a toolkit—complete with white gloves and magnifying glass—for students to use while examining documents!

★ *Treasure Hunt*

Choose from several options for a group treasure hunt.

★ *Documents*

Hunt for the answers to these questions by exploring several documents in the American Memory collection.

★ *Science and Innovation*

This activity introduces students to several fascinating documents related to the development of technology in America.

★ *Who Said What?*

Have students answer these literary questions by exploring several written documents.

★ *What are Primary Sources?*

This learning activity helps students understand the difference between primary and secondary sources.

★ *Why Use Primary Sources?*

Why are primary resources so important? Print out this handout of five illustrated reasons to share with your students.

http://lcweb2.loc.gov/learn/educators/handouts/prsrc.pdf

★ *What Is It?*

Let students view images of innovations that changed our lives.

http://lcweb2.loc.gov/ammem/ndlpedu/educators/workshop/discover/what.html

23.2

★ *Artifact Road Show: Constructing the Context by Mary Ritter*

This online lesson introduces the use of primary resources—where to find them, what they are, how to examine them, and how to "construct the context" to tell the whole story.

http://memory.loc.gov/ammem/ndlpedu/lessons/99/road/intro.html

★ *Evaluating Primary Sources*

Explore this site before sharing it with the group. As a group activity, follow the steps for evaluating primary sources.

http://lcweb2.loc.gov/ammem/ndlpedu/educators/workshop/primary/

From this page, explore other options listed with your class.

★ *How Does it Read?*

Students learn to critically analyze documents and ask questions about what they are reading.

★ *What Do You Hear?*

Students develop critical listening skills.

★ *What Do You See?*

Students learn how to look critically at visual images.

Advertisements Through the Ages

Students will analyze advertisements from the past and compare and contrast them with current advertisements.

Emergence of Advertising in America: 1850–1920

This collection features over 9,000 images related to early advertising. These materials, drawn from the Rare Book, Manuscript, and Special Collections Library at Duke University, include cookbooks, photographs of billboards, print advertisements, trade cards, calendars, almanacs, and leaflets for a multitude of products.

http://memory.loc.gov/ammem/award98/ncdhtml/eaahome.html

Activities:

★ *Analyze an Advertisement*

Give each student a copy of the activity page and the Primary Resource Companion on page 6.

★ *Online Ad Activity*

Go to the American Memory newsletter, The Source, to access the article entitled "Off and Running With Primary Sources."

Print copies of the five ads and worksheets.

Divide students into five groups. Have them complete the worksheets as a group.

http://learning.loc.gov/learn/community/am_newsletter/article.php?id= 8&catname=teaching%20ideas

★ *Comparison Shopping*

Give each student a copy of the activity page.

Analyze an Advertisement

1. Go to "Collection Descriptions" of the *Emergence of Advertising in America: 1850–1920* website.

   http://scriptorium.lib.duke.edu/eaa/browse.html

2. Scroll down to view the categories within the collection.

3. Explore a category.
   Click on "Browse this category."

4. List a category and six subjects you found there.

   _____

   _____

5. Click on a subject heading to view ads for that topic.

6. Check out several categories.

7. Find an advertisement that interests you.

8. Click on "Enlarge" to see the image better.

9. Print a copy of the enlarged ad.

10. Why did you select this ad? _____

    _____

11. Analyze your ad by completing the Primary Resource Companion.

Comparison Shopping

1. Go to "Collection Descriptions" of the *Emergence of Advertising in America: 1850–1920* website.

http://scriptorium.lib.duke.edu/eaa/browse.html

2. Scroll down to view the categories within the collection.

3. Explore a category by clicking on "Browse this category."

4. Click on a subject heading to view ads for that topic.

5. Find an advertisement for a product that interests you and which would still be for sale today in a more modern version.

6. Click on "Enlarge" to see the image better.

7. Print a copy of the enlarged ad.

8. Find a current ad for a similar product in a newspaper or magazine, or on the Internet.

Compare and contrast the two ads.

★ List five or more ways the two ads are similar.

_____

_____

_____

_____

_____

_____

★ List five or more ways the two ads are different.

_____

_____

_____

_____

_____

_____

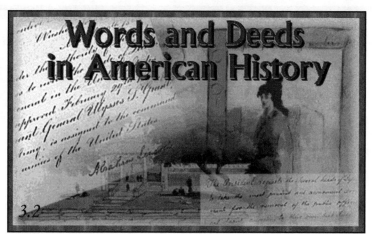

Students analyze a Civil War photo album and research the historical importance of the people included in the album.

Words and Deeds in American History

This collection contains 90 documents dating from the fifteenth century to mid-twentieth century. It includes papers of presidents, Cabinet ministers, members of Congress, Supreme Court justices, military officers, diplomats, reformers, political activists, artists, writers, scientists, inventors, and other prominent Americans whose lives reflect our country's evolution.

http://lcweb2.loc.gov/ammem/mcchtml/corhome.html

Civil War Photograph Album

http://lcweb2.loc.gov/cgi-bin/query/r?ammem/mcc:@field(DOCID+@lit(mcc/051))

Activities:

★ *Explore a Civil War Photo Album*

Give each student a copy of the activity page.

Answers: A. Cartomania
B. views of favorite places and sites
C. John Hay/Abraham Lincoln
D. 25

★ *Research Civil War Portraits*

Give each student a copy of the activity page.

Explore a Civil War Photo Album

3.1 *Abraham Lincoln*

1. Go to the online digital reproduction of the *Civil War Photograph Album.*

    http://lcweb2.loc.gov/cgi-bin/query/r?ammem/mcc:@field(DOCID+@lit(mcc/051)

    This album contains over 200 *cartes de visites* (miniature 2½" x 4" photo portraits often used as calling cards in the mid 1800s.)

2. Read the explanation about the album and its contents. Then answer the questions.

    A. Collecting these cards became a fad in the 1860s called _____.

    B. Besides images of people, what other types of cards did people collect?

        _____

    C. This album was probably assembled by _____, personal secretary to

        _____.

    D. How many pages were in the album? _____

3. Click on the small album image at the top left of the page.

    From this page, select "View these cartes." The front and back of each carte can be viewed in detail. Each image can be enlarged and printed.

    A. How are these 1800s cards like sports or other types of trading cards people collect today?

        _____

        _____

        _____

Name _____ Date _____

Research Civil War Portraits

1. Go to the online digital reproduction of the *Civil War Photograph Album*.

http://lcweb2.loc.gov/cgi-bin/query/r?ammem/mcc:@field(DOCID+@lit(mcc/051))

2. Click on the small album image at the top left of the page.

From this page, select "View these cartes." The front and back of each carte can be viewed in detail. Each image can be enlarged and printed.

3. Print an enlarged image of one person.

4. Use additional resources, like an encyclopedia, to learn more about the person.

Name of person: _____

Date of birth: _____

Date of death: _____

Name of photographer: _____

Location of studio: _____

Is the card autographed? _____

What other written clues are on the card? _____

_____

What is the historical significance of the person?_____

_____

_____

Why do you think that person was included in the album? _____

_____

_____

_____

If you could have an autographed card of any person, past or present, who would it be?

_____

_____

Alphabet Book of the North American Indian

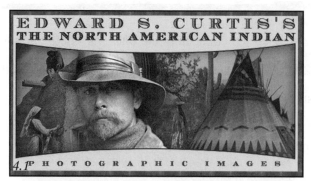

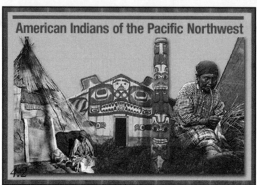

Students examine photographs portraying the life and culture of Native Americans and create an alphabet book to illustrate each letter.

Edward S. Curtis's The North American Indian

In over 2,000 photogravure plates, along with narrative, Curtis portrayed the traditional customs and culture of 80 Indian tribes. The 20 volumes, each with an accompanying portfolio, are organized by tribes and culture areas encompassing the Great Plains, Great Basin, Plateau Region, Southwest, California, Pacific Northwest, and Alaska.

Featured are all of his published photogravure images including over 1,500 illustrations bound in the text volumes, along with over 700 portfolio plates.

http://memory.loc.gov/ammem/award98/ienhtml/curthome.html

American Indians in the Pacific Northwest

This collection features over 2,300 additional photos relating to the Native Americans in the Pacific Northwest.

http://memory.loc.gov/ammem/award98/wauhtml/aipnhome.html

Edward Curtis in Context

http://memory.loc.gov/ammem/award98/ienhtml/special.html

18

Activities:

★ *Native American Alphabet Book*

Give students a copy of the activity page, construction paper, scissors, and glue.

Assign one letter of the alphabet to each student. If you have less than 26 students, offer volunteers extra credit for doing more than one letter.

Compile photos and paragraphs in a three-ring binder to make a class book, or post them in the hall in alphabetical order.

Students can locate additional photographs in the American Indians in the Pacific Northwest collection or search all American Memory collection (limit to photos and prints) using the key word "Native Americans."

★ *ABC Reader's Theater*

Arrange students in alphabetical order by photo selection. Have them take turns presenting their photos and reading their written paragraphs.

Go to the Omaha Indian Music collection which features traditional Omaha music from the 1890s and 1980s.

Download sound files to play quietly in the background during the presentations.

http://memory.loc.gov/ammem/omhhtml/omhhome.html

Native American Alphabet Book

1. Go to the *Edward Curtis Collection.*

http://memory.loc.gov/ammem/award98/ienhtml/curthome.html

2. Browse the collection by subject. Photos are grouped into many categories including persons; social status and occupations; activities; customs and rituals; clothing; headgear; jewelry; weapons; tools; transportation; travel; and settlements and structures.

3. Locate three to five photos for your assigned letter.

Print the photos, trim, and mount them on colored paper.

4. Write a short statement for each photo.

Example:

A is for an ARMLET.   B is for Nez Perce BABE.

5. On another sheet of paper, write a short paragraph to answer these questions about one of your photos.

★ Who is in the photograph?
★ Who took the photo?
★ What does the photo show?
★ What tribe is represented?
★ Where was the photo taken?
★ When was the photo taken?
★ Why do you think the photographer took this picture?
★ Why did you choose this photo?

American Girl Doll Connections

Students explore the American Memory collection to locate photographs and maps that correspond with the time period during which each of the fictional American Girl dolls lived.

Map Collections: 1500–Present

A selection of hundreds of maps digitized from the 4.5 million maps in the Library of Congress Geography and Map Division collections.

http://memory.loc.gov/ammem/gmdhtml/gmdhome.html

By Popular Demand: Portraits of Presidents and First Ladies—1789–Present

http://memory.loc.gov/ammem/odmdhtml/preshome.html

American Memory Timeline

Links, arranged chronologically, lead to sets of selected primary sources on a variety of topics in United States History.

http://memory.loc.gov/ammem/ndlpedu/features/timeline/index.html

Jump Back in Time

Visit different eras in American history.

http://www.americaslibrary.gov/cgi-bin/page.cgi/jb

Time line of Presidents and First Ladies

Each president and first lady is listed chronologically according to the president's term(s) in office.

http://memory.loc.gov/ammem/odmdhtml/pptime.html

Activities:

★ *American Girl Photo Collage*

Familiarize the class with the American Girl dolls and literature. Books can be borrowed from the library and students can be invited to bring in their own dolls.

Each of the dolls and books focuses on a different period in American history.

Felicity (1774—Colonial Period)
Josephina (1824—Southwest Frontier)
Kirsten (1854—Pioneer America)
Addy (1864—Civil War)
Samantha (1904—Turn of the Century)
Kit (1934—Great Depression)
Molly (1944—World War Two)

Have students examine the books for historical information. Each book features a helpful "Peek into the Past" section at the end of the book.

Divide students into seven groups. Have them brainstorm words and phrases to describe one of the seven American Girl characters. Include topics such as...

where the character lived
when the character lived
events in the US during that time period.

Have students go to the Pleasant Company website to learn more about each character and explore their worlds.

http://americangirl.com/sitemap.html

Provide poster board, scissors, and glue.

Have them create a photo collage for each doll with photos found in the collections.

★ **22**

★ *Map the American Girls*

Give each student a copy of the activity page.

Have students keep the completed activity to use with the activities "American Girl Timeline" and "Who Was President?"

★ **American Girl Timeline**

Give each student a copy of the activity page.

Students can combine the material they printed to create a visual timeline as a wall or bulletin board display.

★ *Who Was President?*

Give each student a copy of the activity page.

Have students print copies of the presidents and first ladies, date them, and add them to the timeline.

Map the American Girls

1. Go to the *American Girl* website.

    http://americangirl.com/sitemap.html

2. Click on information for each character to find when and where they lived.

Name	When	Where
Felicity	_____	_____
Josephina	_____	_____
Kirsten	_____	_____
Addy	_____	_____
Samantha	_____	_____
Kit	_____	_____
Molly	_____	_____

2. Go to the *Map Collections: 1500–Present* homepage.

    http://memory.loc.gov/ammem/gmdhtml/gmdhome.html

3. Select the "Cities and Towns" section to locate period maps of each doll's hometown.

4. Click on "Search."

5. Type in the name of the city. Enter.

6. Select the map with the date closest to the one you want.

7. Explore the maps for each American Girl doll.

8. Print one of the maps.

9. Save this page to use with the next two activities.

American Girl Timeline

1. Go to the *American Memory Timeline* site.

   http://memory.loc.gov/ammem/ndlpedu/features/timeline/index.html

   or

   Jump Back in Time

   http://www.americaslibrary.gov/cgi-bin/page.cgi/jb

2. Find the time period for one of the American Girl dolls.

   Name: _____

   Dates: _____

3. Search the timeline. Find six events that happened during this time period.

   Date   Event

   _____

   _____

   _____

   _____

   _____

   _____

4. Print photos or documents related to each event.

5. Label each event with the date and place.

Who Was President?

1. Go to *By Popular Demand: Portraits of Presidents and First Ladies—1789–Present.*

   http://memory.loc.gov/ammem/odmdhtml/preshome.html

2. Click on the link to jump to the *Special Presentation—Time line of Presidents and First Ladies.*

   http://memory.loc.gov/ammem/odmdhtml/pptime.html

3. Scroll through the list to locate the dates during which each girl lived to find the names of the presidents and first ladies.

   Felicity

   President: _____

   First lady: _____

   Josephina

   President: _____

   First lady: _____

   Kirsten

   President: _____

   First lady: _____

   Addy

   President: _____

   First lady: _____

   Samantha

   President: _____

   First lady: _____

   Kit

   President: _____

   First lady: _____

   Molly

   President: _____

   First lady: _____

America's Story from America's Library

6.1

Students visit America's Library and view photos, documents, sound files, and movies from America's past.

America's Story from America's Library

From this site, you can jump to any of the featured sites listed below.

http://www.americaslibrary.gov/cgi-bin/page.cgi

★ *Meet Amazing Americans*

Students can read stories and view primary resources related to famous Americans, go on a President's Scavenger Hunt, or play the Dynamite Presidents game!

★ *Jump Back in Time*

What happened when? Students can access an easy-to-use timeline feature to learn about the important eras in American History, find out what happened on their birthdays, send an historic electronic postcard, or play the Super Sleuth game!

★ *See, Hear, and Sing*

Students can watch old movies, listen to songs, view photos and film clips of some of nature's disasters, laugh at examples of historic humor, or listen to the sounds of some uncommon instruments!

★ *Explore the States*

Students can view documents and read stories about each of our 50 states, go on a state Treasure Hunt, or answer a Quick Quiz question!

★ *Join America at Play*

Students can learn about our celebrations, holidays, and hobbies through historic photos and documents, play the Batter Up game, answer a Quick Quiz question, or send an electronic postcard.

Activities:

★ *Explore America's Story*

Give each student a copy of the activity page.

After students complete the activity, ask several of them to read their answers for the same site to give classmates more ideas about what else could be found at each one.

★ *Write a Review*

After students complete the activity "Explore America's Story," ask them to select the one they liked the most or the least. Have them go back and spend more time on that site, then write a review of the site.

Post the reviews for other students to read.

★ *Go On a Scavenger Hunt*

Give each student two 3" x 5" index cards.

As students complete the activity "Explore America's Story," have them write a question on one card that could be answered at one of the sites.

On the second card, have them write the answer and the address of the website where they found the information.

Have students trade question cards and go on a scavenger hunt to find the answers.

Explore America's Story

1. Go to *America's Story from America's Library*.

From this site, you can jump to any of the featured sites listed below by clicking on the link at the top of the page.

http://www.americaslibrary.gov/cgi-bin/page.cgi

2. Explore each site. List several examples of the types of information you found there.

America's Story from America's Library

_____

_____

Meet Amazing Americans

_____

_____

Jump Back in Time

_____

_____

Explore the States

_____

_____

Join America at Play

_____

_____

See, Hear, and Sing

_____

_____

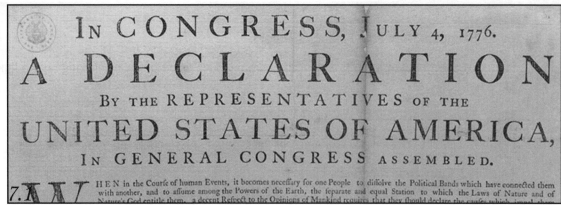

TEACHER PAGE

Students examine important documents in American History.

American Treasures of the Library of Congress
This online exhibit allows you to examine more than 250 historic treasures which are on permanent display in the Thomas Jefferson Building in Washington, DC.

http://www.loc.gov/exhibits/treasures/

America's Top Treasures Gallery
One top treasure will always be on permanent display in the Library of Congress, but due to the fragility of the documents, each one can be displayed for only limited periods of time. This site makes these treasures available to everyone at any time.

http://www.loc.gov/exhibits/treasures/tr00.html

Activities:

★ *America's Top Treasures Hunt*

Give each student a copy of the activity page.
Students will need poster board, scissors, markers, and glue.

★ *Top Treasures Exhibit Gallery*

Display completed posters to create an American Treasures gallery exhibit. As a class, take a walk through the gallery.

America's Top Treasures Hunt

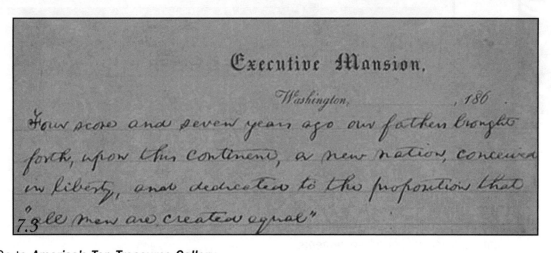

1. Go to *America's Top Treasures Gallery.*

http://www.loc.gov/exhibits/treasures/tr00.html

2. Select one of the following "treasures."

Declaration of Independence
Mason's Declaration of Rights
George Washington's Commission
Emancipation Proclamation
Columbus' Book of Privileges
The Gettysburg Address
Lincoln's First Inaugural Address
Huexotzinco Codex

3. Print an enlarged copy of the document including the written material about the document.

4. Answer these questions about the document on scrap paper.

Who wrote the document?
Who signed the document?
What is the purpose of the document?
When was the document written?
Where was the document signed?
Why is this document important in American history?

5. Use the copy of the document and answers to your questions to create a poster.

Be creative as you design your poster.
Write answers in different colored markers or at different angles.
Add your own drawings, maps, or other related art downloaded from the American Memory collection.

31

Animation Analysis

8.1

Students examine examples of early animation and compare them to animation used in today's cartoons, movies, or advertisements.

Origins of American Animation

Animation had its beginnings in the early 19th century and continues to fascinate both children and adults. This collection features 21 animated films produced between 1900 and 1921.

http://memory.loc.gov/ammem/oahtml/oahome.html

Activities:

★ *Animation Timeline*

Give each student a copy of the activity page.

Assign one year between 1900 and 1921 to each student.

Prepare a classroom or hall wall display by writing each year on separate sheets of paper and taping them to the wall in chronological order. Have students display the material they found under the appropriate year.

★ *Let's Go to the Movies*

Select three to five of the online animated films for an all-class screening. View the films in chronological order.

http://memory.loc.gov/ammem/oahtml/oachron.html

Hint: It is easier to download films in advance.

After viewing each film, give students a few minutes to answer the questions on the activity page.

Hold a group discussion comparing one of the films to a current animation on a similar topic.

Animation Timeline

Work with your classmates to create a visual timeline of animation.

1. Go to *Notes on the Origins of Early Animation, 1900–1921*

http://memory.loc.gov/ammem/oahtml/oapres.html

2. Find information on animation for one specific year between 1900 and 1921. Be certain to include basic developments and changes in animation techniques.

3. Write your information on another sheet of paper.

4. Print copies of drawings and other interesting items related to animation for the same year.

Let's Go to the Movies

View some of the online films individually or as a class. For each film, write answers to these questions on another sheet of paper.

★ What was the name of the film?
★ When was it made?
★ What message was the film trying to convey?
★ Do you think the film communicated this message successfully? Why or why not?
★ What animation techniques were used?
★ What did you notice in the film that tells something about life in the U.S. at the time this film was made?

Book Backdrops—Making Literature Connections

Students locate, analyze, and display photographs that provide visual links to non-fiction or historical fiction literature.

Collections used will depend on the historical setting of the literature. The American Memory "Collections Finder" page can be especially helpful for locating collections related to a specific time period. Categories include events, people, places, time, or topic.

http://memory.loc.gov/ammem/collections/finder.html

Activities:

★ *Historical Reading*

Use the literature suggestions at the end of this section or select titles that fit your students' curriculum and reading levels.

Before reading the book as a class, discuss its historical setting.

Brainstorm words and events related to that period.

After reading the book, brainstorm again to extend this list.

Finally, direct the students to a specific collection where they can search for photographs and other visual images related to the time period of the book.

Have students print one visual image related to the book and write a statement explaining how the image relates to the book.

Display a copy of the cover of the book and surround it with images and students' statements.

Literature suggestions:

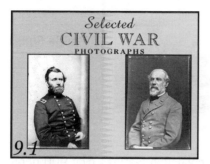

Pink and Say by Patricia Polacco

Selected Civil War Photographs: This collection contains over 1,000 photographs, most of which were made under Mathew Brady's supervision.

http://memory.loc.gov/ammem/cwphtml/cwphome.html

In the Year of the Boar and Jackie Robinson by Bette Lord

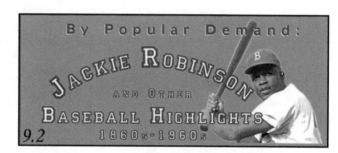

Go to *Jackie Robinson and Other Baseball Highlights 1860s–1960s.* This collection features materials highlighting Jackie Robinson's story and baseball history in general.

http://memory.loc.gov/ammem/jrhtml/jrhome.html

Gold Fever: Tales from the California Gold Rush by Rosalyn Schanzer

The Journal of Wong Ming-Chung: A Chinese Miner by Lawrence Yep

California As I Saw It—First Person Narratives of California's Early Years, 1849–1900: This collection features texts and illustrations of 190 works documenting early California through eyewitness accounts.

http://memory.loc.gov/ammem/cbhtml/cbhome.html

Prairie Songs by Pam Conrad

The Northern Great Plains, 1880–1920: This collection features over 900 photos of turn-of-the-century prairie life.

http://memory.loc.gov/ammem/award97/ndfahtml/ngphome.html

You Forgot Your Skirt, Amelia Bloomer by Shana Corey

A Time for Courage by Kathryn Lasky

Votes for Women—Suffrage Pictures, 1850–1920—a visual presentation of the women's suffrage movement.

http://memory.loc.gov/ammem/vfwhtml/vfwhome.html

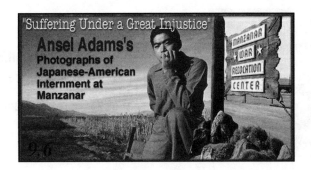

Farewell to Manzanar by Jeanne Wakatsuki Houston and James D. Houston

Suffering under a Great Injustice: Ansel Adams's Photographs of Japanese American Internment at Manzanar to view Ansel Adams documents of the Manzanar War Relocation Center.

http://memory.loc.gov/ammem/aamhtml/aamhome.html

Buildings and Structures

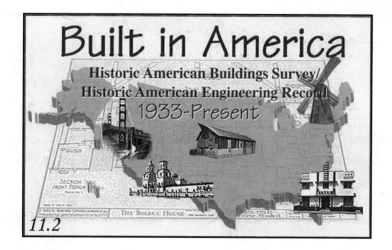

Students analyze building styles and materials in relation to geographic location and historic era.

Built in America: Historic American Buildings Survey/Historic American Engineering Record 1933–Present

This collection documents achievements in architecture, engineering, and design in the United States.

http://memory.loc.gov/ammem/hhhtml/hhhome.html

Activities:

★ *Stately Structures*

Assign three to five different states to each student.

Give each student a copy of the activity page.

Additional buildings can be located by viewing the Geographic Location index.

http://memory.loc.gov/ammem/hhhtml/hhgeogindex.html

Have students share their findings with the class and display images around a state map.

Create a class book of maps and images in a three-ring binder.

★ *Time and Place Literature Connections*

Structures can also be located by searching using a subject keyword (slavery, civil war) or geographic location (state, county, city). This strategy can be used to make literature connections to non-fiction or historical fiction literature.

Stately Structures

1. Go to the *HABS/HAER Image Gallery Map and Geographic Listings*.

http://memory.loc.gov/ammem/hhhtml/hhmap.html

2. Locate and print a photo of one building from each state assigned to you.

3. Study each photo. On the back of the photo, answer these questions. Use additional reference materials if needed.

Who designed the building?

Why was the building constructed (purpose)?

When was it built?

Where is it located?

What materials were used to build it?

What building shape, roof shape, or architectural style do you observe?

What special design features does it have?

What does the building tell about the geographical location and era in which it was built?

Calendar Connections

Students illustrate calendar projects with primary resources from the American Memory collection.

Today in History
Updated daily, this site features primary sources related to every day of the year.

http://memory.loc.gov/ammem/today/today.html

Jump Back in Time
Choose "Pick a Date" from this page to locate historic events for each day of the year.

http://www.americaslibrary.gov/cgi-bin/page.cgi/jb

American Memory Timeline Feature
Sets of links, arranged in chronological order, lead to selected primary sources on a variety of topics in U. S. history.

http://memory.loc.gov/ammem/ndlpedu/features/timeline/index.html

Activities:

★ *Daily Reporter*

This activity is a great way to integrate primary sources into the classroom on a daily basis. Each day, assign a different student to consult *Today in History* or *Jump Back in Time.*

Ask the "Daily Reporter" to orally share a report of several historic events that occurred on that day with the class.

Happy Birthday! and Birthday Quilt

Give each student a copy of the activity page and the Primary Resource Companion on page 6.

Students will need large squares of construction paper, scissors, and glue.

Combine the quilt squares to make a group birthday quilt display.

Students can present a brief oral summary of the event to the class on their birthdays. Pick a day near the end of the year for those with summer birthdays.

Classroom Historical Photo Calendar

Locate a blank calendar grid. Most word processing software programs include a calendar template. Free calendar grids can also be located online using the search term "calendar template."

Divide the class into groups. Assign a specific month to each group.

Distribute blank calendar templates and a copy of the activity page.

Compile the finished pages into a class calendar to be used throughout the school year.

Calendars can be created to feature a specific time period (Civil War, Pioneer Life, etc.), a specific event, famous people, or a geographic location.

Optional: Instead of creating a calendar for the entire year, this could be designed as a monthly activity with each student researching one or two days.

Happy Birthday!

Pick a date to visit!
How about your
BIRTHDAY?

January
1   GO   *12.3*

1. Go to *Today in History*.

   http://memory.loc.gov/ammem/today/today.html

2. Select the day and month you were born.

3. Select one event that happened on your birthday.

4. Print out the primary source featured for this date.

5. Complete a Primary Resource Companion sheet.

Birthday Quilt

1. Use visual images from the material you printed to create a construction paper "quilt square."

2. Write your birthday on the square in fancy letters.

3. Cut photos, text, maps, and other images from material for events on your birthday into interesting shapes. Glue them to your quilt square.

4. Combine your quilt square with your classmates' to create a group birthday quilt.

Classroom Historical Photo Calendar

Work with a group to create a photo calendar of historical events for a specific month.

1. Divide the days of the assigned month among members of the group. Each person will need to find information for several days.

2. Go to *Today in History*.

http://memory.loc.gov/ammem/today/today.html

3. Select the specific days for the month that you will be completing.

4. Browse through the events listed for each day.

5. Select one event for each day. Write it on your group calendar.

Example for December 16 entry: Boston Tea Party: 1773.

6. As a group, select one photo or visual image from the American Memory collection to go with your calendar page.

7. Print a copy of the photo and attach it to the top of the calendar page.

What image did your group decide to use? _____

Who is shown in the image? _____

What event is shown? _____

When did the event take place? _____

Why did your group select this image? _____

Caption It!

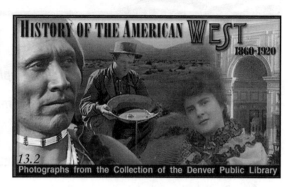

Students write captions and short news articles to accompany American Memory photographs.

Touring Turn-of-the-Century America: Photographs from the Detroit Publishing Company 1880–1920

This collection features over 25,000 photos of scenes taken in the United States: scenic, historic, and even some humorous ones.

http://memory.loc.gov/ammem/detroit/dethome.html

History of the American West, 1860–1920

This collection includes over 30,000 photos taken primarily west of the Mississippi River.

http://memory.loc.gov/ammem/award97/codhtml/hawphome.html

Activities:

★ *Funny Photo Card*

Give each student a copy of the activity page and a piece of folded card stock. They will also need scissors and glue.

Combine this with a letter writing unit. Have students write letters and mail them with the funny photo cards to a friend or relative.

★ *Disaster Strikes!*

Give each student a copy of the activity and the Sample Questions for Primary Resources Analysis on page 8.

Prepare a display of the photos and captions.

Option: Display the photos without captions. Give each student one caption and have them match the caption to the correct photo.

Funny Photo Card

Sites to visit:

Touring Turn-of-the-Century America: Photographs from the Detroit Publishing Company 1880–1920

http://memory.loc.gov/ammem/detroit/dethome.html

History of the American West, 1860–1920

http://memory.loc.gov/ammem/award97/codhtml/hawphome.html

1. Search these two collections using the terms "humorous pictures," "humorous photographs," or "animals in human situations."

2. Browse through the photos.

3. Select and print a photo you think is funny.

4. Make notes about what you observe in the photo. (Who is pictured? What is happening? Why is it funny? etc.)

   _____

   _____

   _____

   _____

5. Write a short humorous caption to go with your photo.

   A humorous caption can be one or two sentences describing the photograph. Good captions are written in present tense. They grab attention by using strong nouns and colorful action verbs.

   _____

   _____

   _____

6. Attach the photo to folded cardstock and add the caption below the picture.

Disaster Strikes!

Sites to visit:

Touring Turn-of-the-Century America: Photographs from the Detroit Publishing Company 1880–1920

http://memory.loc.gov/ammem/detroit/dethome.html

History of the American West, 1860–1920

http://memory.loc.gov/ammem/award97/codhtml/hawphome.html

1. Search these two collections using the term "disaster" or words such as flood, earthquake, fire, or blizzard.

2. Browse through the photos. Select and print a photo you think is interesting.

3. Use the Sample Questions for Primary Resource Analysis page to make notes about what you observe in the photo.

_____

_____

_____

_____

_____

_____

_____

4. Write a two- or three-sentence factual caption to describe the photograph. Good captions are written in present tense. They use strong nouns and colorful action verbs to grab attention. Include who, what, when, where, why, and how information.

_____

_____

_____

_____

_____

_____

TEACHER PAGE

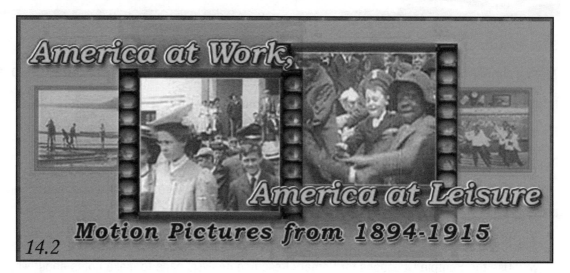

America at Work, America at Leisure
Motion Pictures from 1894-1915
14.2

Students explore the types of work people did in the late 19th and early 20th century.

America at Work, America at Leisure

This collection features 150 short movies depicting work, school, and leisure in the United States in the late 19th and early 20th centuries.

http://memory.loc.gov/ammem/awlhtml/awlhome.html

America at Work, 1894–1915

http://memory.loc.gov/ammem/awlhtml/awlwork.html

Activities:

★ *Americans At Work*

Give each student a copy of the activity page.

★ *Help Wanted*

Give each student a copy of the activity page.

Provide Help Wanted sections of local newspapers for students to use as models.

"Cut and paste" student ads to create a Help Wanted section for your class.

Americans at Work

1. Go to *America at Work, 1894–1915.*

   http://memory.loc.gov/ammem/awlhtml/awlwork.html

2. Read the text about working conditions in the U.S. between 1894 and 1915.

3. Investigate several occupations featured in this collection. View at least three short films for one occupation.

4. Select one occupation and answer these questions. Use information you learned from the text and the films.

   Type of job: _____

   What skills were required for this job? _____

   _____

   Did the job involve a high level of responsibility? _____

   _____

   What were working conditions like? _____

   Are people employed in this type of job today? _____

   Would you have chosen this career if you had lived then? Why or why not? _____

   _____

   What three questions do you have about this career that were not answered in the text or film?

   _____

   _____

   _____

Help Wanted

14.1

14.3

1. Go to *America at Work, 1894–1915*.

   http://memory.loc.gov/ammem/awlhtml/awlwork.html

2. View films for at least three occupations featured in this collection.

3. Use current newspapers as models. Create a "Help Wanted Ad" for three jobs featured in this collection.

   Each ad should include the title of the job, required qualifications, and contact information.

   Write your ads on the next page.

Help Wanted

_____
_____
_____
_____
_____

Help Wanted

_____
_____
_____
_____
_____
_____
_____
_____
_____
_____
_____
_____

Help Wanted

_____
_____
_____
_____
_____
_____
_____

Cartoons and Caricatures

Students examine cartoons and caricatures as examples of primary sources that reflect political views throughout history.

Oliphant's Anthem—Pat Oliphant at the Library of Congress

This exhibit includes early works, war and diplomacy cartoons, presidential campaigns, Richard Nixon, sketchbooks, domestic issues, recent works, and the "Socks Album."

http://lcweb.loc.gov/exhibits/oliphant/oliphant.html

Herblock's History: Political Cartoons from the Crash to the Millennium

Herbert Block, better known as Herblock, was a well-known editorial cartoonist who worked for the *Washington Post* for 55 years.

http://www.loc.gov/rr/print/swann/herblock/

Activities:

★ *View a Political Cartoon by Pat Oliphant*

As a class, complete the online activity, *Pat Oliphant's Editorial Cartoons.* Discuss the online questions and the meaning of the word caricature.

http://memory.loc.gov/ammem/ndlpedu/educators/workshop/discover/cartoon.html

★ *Political Cartoons and Caricatures*

Give each student a copy of the activity page and the Primary Resource Companion on page 6.

Post cartoons and statements in your classroom.

Political Cartoons and Caricatures

1. Go to *Oliphant's Anthem—Pat Oliphant at the Library of Congress.*

   http://lcweb.loc.gov/exhibits/oliphant/oliphant.html

2. Search this collection using the terms cartoons, political cartoons, or caricatures.

3. Browse through the collections.

4. Select one cartoon and print it.

5. Examine the cartoon and complete the Primary Resource Organizer.

6. Write a statement that answers the question: How does this cartoon reflect the social or political situation of the time?

   _____

   _____

   _____

   _____

7. Go to *Herblock's History: Political Cartoons from the Crash to the Millennium.*

   http://www.loc.gov/rr/print/swann/herblock/

8. Browse through the collection.

9. Select one cartoon and print it.

10. List three ways these two political cartoons are alike.

    _____

    _____

    _____

11. List three ways these two political cartoons are different.

    _____

    _____

    _____

Child Labor in America

Students observe photographs by Lewis Hine and examine children's working conditions during early twentieth-century America.

National Child Labor Committee Collection; Photographs by Lewis Hine (Selected Images)

Lewis Hine worked as an investigative photographer for the National Child Labor Committee and documented working and living conditions of children in the United States between 1908 and 1921. This photographic collection is an excellent primary source for studies of reform movements, working class families, and child labor in the U.S.

http://lcweb.loc.gov/rr/print/coll/207-b.html

Activities:

★ **Children at Work**

Give each student a copy of the activity page.

A search of the Prints and Photographs collection, using the terms "Lewis Hine" or "child laborers" will bring up hundreds of additional similar photos.

http://lcweb2.loc.gov/pp/mdbquery.html

Students can use the same photograph for the Child Labor Cinquain activity.

As a group, discuss how life today is very different for children.

★ **Child Labor Cinquain**

Give each student a copy of the activity page.

Display photographs with cinquains.

52

Name _____ Date _____

Children at Work

1. Go to the *National Child Labor Committee Collection; Photographs by Lewis Hine.*

Lewis Hine worked as an investigative photographer for the National Child Labor Committee. He documented working and living conditions of children in the United States between 1908 and 1921.

http://lcweb.loc.gov/rr/print/coll/207-b.html

2. Browse through the collection to find photos featuring children. Photographs can be enlarged for closer study.

3. List six jobs children did that are shown in the photographs. _____

_____

_____

4. Print one enlarged photograph you find interesting and information about the photograph. Answer these questions.

Who is pictured in the photo? (Describe what you see.) _____

_____

_____

What type of work is the child in the photo doing?_____

_____

When was the photo taken? _____

Where was the photo taken? _____

Why do you think Lewis Hine took this photo? _____

_____

How does this photo make you feel?_____

What if you were the child in the photo? _____

_____

_____

Keep the copy of the photograph to use with the next activity.

Child Labor Cinquain

1. Use the photograph of a child at work from the last activity or select a different one.

2. Create a cinquain poem to describe your photo.

Use powerful descriptive words and rhyming words or repeated words for emphasis.

Cinquain format to use:

First line—two syllables (describing the photo)

Second line—four syllables (describing the work being done)

Third line—six syllables (expressing the action in the picture)

Fourth line—eight syllables (describing how you feel about doing this job)

Fifth line—two syllables (describing the photo)

17.3

(Shrimp and Oyster Worker, Biloxi, Miss.
Lewis Hine, photographer. 1911)

Sample poem:
Young boy
Shrimp and oysters
Finding, digging, carrying
Exhausting, smelly, cold, heavy
Hard work.

1. Write a rough draft of your poem on scrap paper.

2. Edit your poem. Write the final copy on good paper. Don't forget to add a title.

18.1

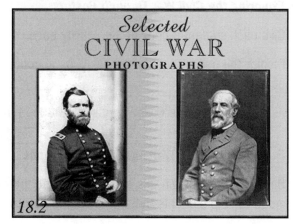

18.2

Students locate, examine, and analyze Civil War documents and photographs.

Civil War Treasures From the NY Historical Society
This extensive collection features links to letters, stereographs, photographs, sketches, posters, and envelopes from the Civil War era.

http://memory.loc.gov/ammem/ndlpcoop/nhihtml/cwnyhshome.html

Selected Civil War Photographs
This collection includes more than 1,000 photographs, most of which were made under Mathew Brady's supervision. Photos include battle scenes, military and personal artifacts, and pictures of soldiers and officers.

http://memory.loc.gov/ammem/cwphtml/cwphome.html

Photojournalism: A Record of War
http://lcweb2.loc.gov/ammem/ndlpedu/lessons/97/photo/analysis.html

Activities:

★ *Exploring the Civil War Through Envelopes*

To provide background information for students, print Before, During, and After the Civil War, a chronological overview of the Civil War period.

http://memory.loc.gov/ammem/ndlpcoop/nhihtml/cwnyhsspec.html

Give each student a copy of the activity page.

Display the envelopes and statements in chronological order.

★ *Exploring the Civil War Through Posters*

Give each student a copy of the activity page.

Display the posters for class viewing. As a group, compare and contrast several of the posters.

As a group, compare Civil War posters with current posters enlisting support for a cause.

★ *Exploring the Civil War Through Photographs*

Before students begin this activity, complete the online lesson "What Do You See?" as a group to help students better understand how to analyze a photograph in detail.

http://lcweb2.loc.gov/ammem/ndlpedu/lessons/97/civilwar/civilwar.html

Give each student a copy of the activity page.

Ask a group of students to prepare a Civil War Gallery of photographs arranged in chronological order. Include students' letters and journal entries.

As a class, take a walk through the gallery. Ask the student who selected each photograph to tell the group when and where the photo was taken and briefly discuss his or her observations of the photo.

Exploring the Civil War Through Envelopes

1. Go to *Civil War Treasures From the New York Historical Society.*

   http://memory.loc.gov/ammem/ndlpcoop/nhihtml/cwnyhshome.html

2. Click on the link to "Archival Collections."

3. Click on the link to "Civil War Envelopes" in the Prints and Posters section.

4. Click on "list items" to view 490 envelopes with images related to Civil War events and personalities.

5. Select several envelopes to examine in detail. Enlarge and print each envelope.

6. Read the summary information for each envelope to find clues about why it is important to Civil War history.

7. On the back of each printout, write a statement which answers the following questions:

   What images are on the envelope? (Images may include caricatures of politicians, slogans, portraits, flags, state seals, animals, sailors, soldiers, and camp scenes.)

   How do the images relate to events during the Civil War?

Exploring the Civil War Through Posters

1. Go to *Civil War Treasures from the New York Historical Society.*

   http://memory.loc.gov/ammem/ndlpcoop/nhihtml/cwnyhshome.html

2. Click on the link to "Archival Collections."

3. Click on the link to the Civil War Poster Collection in the Prints and Posters section.

4. Click on "list items" to find 304 posters dating from the beginning of the Civil War through March 1865.

5. Select a poster to study. Print out an enlarged copy of the poster.

6. Examine the poster and answer the following questions.

   Describe what is pictured in the poster._____

   _____

   _____

   What patriotic images are included? _____

   _____

   What incentives or bonuses were offered to new recruits? _____

   _____

   Was the poster designed to appeal to a particular ethnic group? If yes, which one? _____

   _____

   What pay was offered?_____

   _____

   Was discrimination evident in the poster? If yes, describe. _____

   _____

   _____

   Would this poster have appealed to you if you were living during Civil War times? Why or why not?

   _____

   _____

   _____

Exploring the Civil War Through Photographs

1. Go to the *Selected Civil War Photographs* collection.

   http://memory.loc.gov/ammem/cwphtml/cwphome.html

2. Search the collection by key phrase "Civil War."

3. Select and print one photograph you find interesting.

4. Examine the photograph for details.

5. Write the date, location, and other information about the photograph on the back.

6. Imagine yourself at the scene when the photograph was taken. Complete one of these writing activities.

   Write a first-person journal entry describing the situation in the photo. Include details.

   Write a letter home to your family describing the situation in the photo.

   _____

   _____

   _____

   _____

   _____

   _____

   _____

   _____

   _____

   _____

   _____

   _____

   _____

Clothing and Costumes

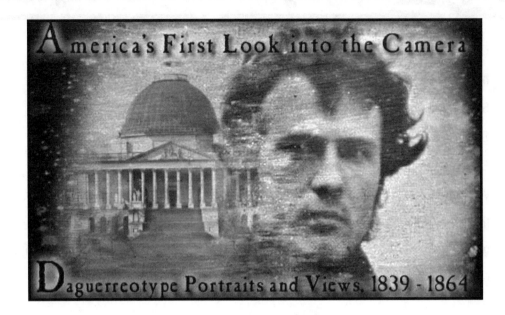

America's First Look into the Camera

Daguerreotype Portraits and Views, 1839 - 1864

Students examine clothing and accessories worn by Americans between 1839 and 1864.

America's First Look into the Camera: Daguerreotype Portraits and Views, 1839–1864

This collection features 725 photographs dating from 1839 to 1864.

http://memory.loc.gov/ammem/daghtml/daghome.html

Activities:

★ *Dressing Up for the Camera*

Give each student a copy of the activity page.

Combine photos and arrange them in a timeline by date of photo.

Hold an 1800s dress-up day using the timeline of photos for costume ideas.

As a group, compare and contrast the clothing worn by people in several photos.

★ *Costumes on Parade*

Is your class studying a specific time period? Do you need costume ideas for a play? Are students dressing up for Halloween?

The Library of Congress collections are full of creative costuming ideas. A search of the American Memory collections using keywords such as costume, uniforms, clothing, and dress will result in hundreds of hits.

Dressing Up for the Camera

24.1

1. Go to *America's First Look into the Camera: Daguerreotype Portraits and Views, 1839–1864.*

   http://memory.loc.gov/ammem/daghtml/daghome.html

2. Browse the subject index.

3. Click on several of the collections to view the images.

4. Select and print two interesting photos that feature only one or two people.

5. Study the details of what the people are wearing, including hats, shoes, and jewelry.

6. On another sheet of paper, write a paragraph about each photo that answers these questions:

   Who is pictured in the photo? (male or female, child or adult)

   What is the person wearing? (details of clothing, hats, shoes, etc.)

   From the expression on the person's face, how do you think this person felt about having his or her picture taken?

   When was the photo taken? (historical time period)

   Where was the photo taken? (location and setting)

7. Label the photos with the title, date taken, and name of the collection where you found them.

Students examine cookbooks, advertisements, photographs, and films related to the early history of consumerism in America.

Emergence of Advertising in America 1850–1920: Advertising Cookbooks

This collection features over 80 advertising cookbooks used as early promotional devices by food companies and appliance manufacturers.

http://scriptorium.lib.duke.edu/eaa/cookbooks.html

Emergence of Advertising in America 1850–1920: Advertising Ephemera Collection

This category contains ephemera such as trading cards, calendars, almanacs, postcards, flyers, and leaflets for a multitude of products.

http://scriptorium.lib.duke.edu/eaa/ephemera.html

An American Time Capsule: Three Centuries of Broadsides and Other Printed Ephemera

This collection features thousands of items including posters, notices, advertisements, menus, proclamations, leaflets, propaganda, manifestos, and business cards dating from the seventeenth century to the present.

http://memory.loc.gov/ammem/rbpehtml/pehome.html

Activities:

★ *Shopping for Memories*

Discuss the term ephemera (items designed to be useful for only a short period of time) with the group. Ask them to name several modern day examples of ephemera.

Give each student a copy of the activity page.

62

★ *Visit a General Store*

If you have not done so already, complete the online lesson "What Do You See?" as a group to help students better understand how to analyze a photograph in detail.

http://lcweb2.loc.gov/ammem/ndlpedu/lessons/97/civilwar/civilwar.html

Give each student a copy of the activity page.

Have students present their commercials to the class.

Extension Activities:

Students can create a product catalog of the selected items.

Students can prepare an order form listing all products with short written descriptions and costs for each item.

★ *Create a Class Cookbook*

Before students begin this activity, share the descriptive information about the cookbooks found at this site.

http://scriptorium.lib.duke.edu/eaa/cookbooks.html

Give each student a copy of the activity page.

Ask a group of students to compile a class cookbook in a three-ring binder. Include the printed covers and recipes students found. Have them decide on a catchy title and prepare a Table of Contents for the book.

Extension Activities:

Students could compile a shopping list for ingredients needed to make their recipes, then go to a grocery store and price the items.

Ask parent volunteers to make some of the recipes in the class cookbook to share with the group.

★ *What's on the Menu?*

Give each student a copy of the activity page.

Share the menus with classmates. As a group, discuss and compare available menu choices and costs.

Discuss how these menus differ from the menus at restaurants the students visit today.

★ *How Much Would it Cost Today?*

Students can use the Inflation Calculator to determine the cost of the meal in today's dollars.

http://www.westegg.com/inflation/

★ *Dining in Style*

Go to *An Animated Luncheon—A 1900 Edison film.*

http://memory.loc.gov/cgi-bin/query/r?ammem/papr:@field
(NUMBER+@band(edmp+1154))

As a group, view this early comedy/drama Edison film featuring a luncheon scene in a fashionable cafe. (Option, download it to the hard drive for later use by individual students.)

After watching the film, have students write a movie review. Ask them to rate it on a scale of 1 to 10.

Shopping for Memories

1. Go to the *Emergence of Advertising in America 1850–1920: Advertising Ephemera Collection.*

   http://scriptorium.lib.duke.edu/eaa/ephemera.html

2. Click on "browse the Advertising Ephemera Category."

3. Browse through the list of categories of products.

4. Look through several ads in categories that interest you.

5. Select one product and print the ad for it.

6. Study the ad and the information about the document.

   Would this product be of interest to people today? Why or why not? _____

   _____

   Is it still for sale? _____

   How do similar products today compare with this product? _____

   _____

   _____

7. On another sheet of paper, write a television or radio commercial for the product to present to the class.

   Include information about who would want to buy the product, special features of the product, where it can be purchased, and how much it cost.

   Your ad should take between one and two minutes to present.

Visit a General Store!

General stores served as gathering places, early post offices, and places to purchase goods.

1. Go to the *American Memory* search page.

http://memory.loc.gov/ammem/mdbquery.html

2. Use the term "general store" to search the collection. Limit your search to photos and prints.

3. Locate images of stores. Browse through the photographs.

4. Select and print one photo that shows an inside view of a general store.

5. Study the photo. Use the information about the photo to answer the questions.

What is the name of the store?_____

Where was it located? _____

When was the store in business? _____

What kinds of products did the store sell?_____

_____

_____

Who might have shopped at this store? _____

_____

How does this store differ from a store of today? _____

_____

_____

How is this store like a store today? _____

_____

_____

Create a Class Cookbook

19.3

1. Go to the *Emergence of Advertising in America 1850–1920: Advertising Cookbooks* site to explore early advertising cookbooks.

   http://scriptorium.lib.duke.edu/eaa/cookbooks.html

2. Browse the collection and select a product category to explore.

3. Click on "View this book" to examine the cookbook in detail.

4. Select one cookbook you find interesting.

5. Use the table of contents on the left to explore enlarged images of individual pages.

6. Locate the following information:

   Title, author, publisher, and date of publication _____

   _____

   What product is the cookbook advertising? _____

   Are recipes or menus included? _____

   What other types of information are included?_____

   _____

   _____

7. Print the cover of the book and an image of the advertised product if available.

8. Select and print two or three recipes that sound tasty—or ones that sound rather unusual!

What's on the Menu?

1. Use the term "menus" to locate menu images in one of the following collections.

   Emergence of Advertising in America 1850–1920

   http://memory.loc.gov/ammem/award98/ncdhtml/eaahome.html

   An American Time Capsule: Three Centuries of Broadsides and Other Printed Ephemera

   http://memory.loc.gov/ammem/rbpehtml/pehome.html

2. Select and print a menu.

3. Label the menu with the restaurant name, location, and date. Use reference materials to research unfamiliar menu items.

4. Write your order for a well-balanced meal that includes a salad, main dish, dessert, and beverage. Write the price of each item on the order form.

Item	Price
_____	_____
_____	_____
_____	_____
_____	_____
_____	_____
_____	_____
Meal Total	_____
Tip (15%)	_____
Total Cost	_____

5. Tally the total for your meal. Add a 15% tip and find the total cost.

Dig into Documents

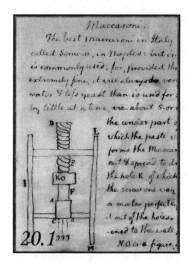

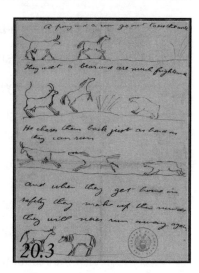

Students examine a variety of types of written documents in the American Memory collection in detail using Primary Resource Companions.

Words and Deeds in American History

This online collection displays approximately 90 selected documents representing the Library of Congress Manuscript Division's first hundred years.

http://lcweb2.loc.gov/ammem/mcchtml/corhome.html

Activities:

★ *Learn about Manuscripts*

Print the special presentation Collecting, Preserving, and Researching History: A Peek into the Library of Congress Manuscript Division.

http://memory.loc.gov/ammem/mcchtml/special.html

Divide students into eight groups. Have each group read and summarize one section of the information and present it to the class.

★ *Please Pass the Macaroni*

Give each student a copy of the activity page.

Answers: A. Thomas Jefferson; ice cream, peach flambe, and macaroons
B. Theodore Roosevelt; play in the barn and go swimming in the beach

★ *A Document-a-Day—The American Memory Way*

Introduce students to *Today in History.*

http://memory.loc.gov/ammem/today/today.html

As a group, visit the site daily for one week and discuss the historic events featured that day.

Print one of the featured documents. As a group, analyze the document using the Sample Questions for Primary Resource Analysis on page 8.

Have each student write a brief summary of the document and include a citation to the original information.

For the rest of the school year, develop a rotating schedule so all students take turns acting as "Daily Historian."

"Daily Historian" job description: Visit the *Today in History* site for a specific day. After reading about the events of the day and viewing the featured documents, select one to print for further analysis using the Sample Questions for Primary Resource Analysis on page 8. Write a summary of the document and present this orally to the class.

Post the "Document of the Day" in a prominent place in your classroom.

At the end of each week, students can compile the daily documents and summary sheets into a three-ring binder titled "Document Yearbook." Include a divider for each month.

At the end of the year, offer the notebook to the library media specialist as a reference for other students.

★ *Dig a Little Deeper*

Give each student a copy of the activity page.

Answers: A. 1714
            B. Margaret Shippen Arnold
            C. 13
            D. "What Hath God Wroght?"
            E. Leave you not the little spot

Please Pass the Macaroni

1. Go to *Words and Deeds in American History.*

http://memory.loc.gov/ammem/mcchtml/corlst.html

2. Click on "Browse the Chronological List" to select a time period, search the collection by keyword, or browse the name and subject index.

3. Find these documents and answer the questions.

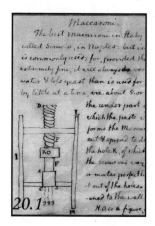

A. Who made this drawing for a macaroni machine and wrote the instructions for making pasta?

_____

Besides macaroni, what other three items did this former president like to serve to his guests?

_____

B. Who wrote this document? _____

On the first page of this letter, the writer asks his son if he would like to do two things. What are they?

_____

_____

Dig a Little Deeper

1. Go to *Words and Deeds in American History.*

   http://memory.loc.gov/ammem/mcchtml/corlst.tml

2. Click on "Browse the Chronological List" to select a time period, search the collection by keyword, or browse the name and subject index.

3. Find these documents and answer the questions.

   Find: An Indian Treaty signed in New Hampshire in 1713.

   A. In what year was a second document signed and attached to this treaty? _____

   Find: Benedict Arnold's 1780 letter to George Washington pleading mercy for his wife.

   B. What was his wife's name?

   _____

   Find: A poem written by Helen Keller to Alexander Graham Bell.

   C. How old was Helen Keller when she wrote this poem? _____

   Find: Samuel Morse's first telegraph message.

   D. What four words did Samuel Morse send in his first telegraph message?

   _____

   Find: A corrected reprint of Walt Whitman's poem, "O Captain! My Captain."

   E. What words were crossed out and replaced with the words "O the bleeding drops of red?"

   _____

It's Ephemeral!

26.1

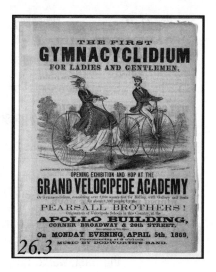

26.3

Students learn the meaning of ephemera and view a variety of examples representing different genres.

An American Time Capsule: Three Centuries of Broadsides and Other Printed Ephemera

This collection features over 28,000 primary source items that provide a unique view of American history. Items include advertisements, broadsides, posters, flyers, clippings, menus, programs, timetables, and other items of a transitory nature.

http://memory.loc.gov/ammem/rbpehtml/pehome.html

Emergence of Advertising in America 1850–1920

This collection includes many examples of ephemera including advertising, broadsides, and scrapbooks.

http://memory.loc.gov/ammem/award98/ncdhtml/eaahome.html

What Can We Learn From Yesterday's Stuff? Exploring the Past Through Printed Ephemera

This online workshop helps students understand how ephemera can be used by historians to understand the past.

http://memory.loc.gov/ammem/ndlpedu/educators/workshop/ephemera/peover.html

Activities:

★ *What is Ephemera?*

Go to the special online presentation: *Introduction to Printed Ephemera Collection.*

http://memory.loc.gov/ammem/rbpehtml/pessay.html

View and discuss the presentation as a class.

Divide chart paper into four columns. Title the columns: Ephemera: Past only: Present only: Both past and present.

Brainstorm a list of items that students consider to be ephemera. Write each item in the Ephemera column. Have students decide if the item would only have been available in the past, would only be available today, or would be available in the past and present. Make a check mark in the appropriate column.

★ *What Can We Learn From Yesterday's Stuff?*

As a class, go to the introduction of this online workshop.

http://memory.loc.gov/ammem/ndlpedu/educators/workshop/ephemera/peintro.html

Click on the word "genre" for a table of ephemera terms, their definitions, and links to samples.

Return to the introduction page and explore the other parts of this section.

Have students add additional items to the group list of ephemera.

★ *Scrapbooking Through the Centuries*

Give each student a copy of the activity page.

★ *Explore a 19th Century Scrapbook!*

Give each student a copy of the activity page.

Scrapbooks can also be browsed by "theme name" from this page:

http://scriptorium.lib.duke.edu/eaa/scrapbooks-themes.html

Extension Activity:

As a culminating activity, create a "replica" class scrapbook. Images can be enlarged, printed in color, cut out, and pasted into a blank scrapbook.

★ **Create a Modern Day Ephemera Scrapbook**

Students can create a group scrapbook with samples of current ephemera that represent their daily lives.

Refer to the list students created of items that would be present-day ephemera. (The list could include advertisements, store receipts, ticket stubs, stamps, invitations, postcards, award stickers, business cards, and other small items that are normally thrown away after use.)

For a week, have each student bring in examples of ephemera from home or school and put them in a large cardboard box. Limit collecting to flat items.

Have students separate the items into the categories on their brainstormed list. Add to the list as needed.

Divide the students into groups to create scrapbook pages with selected items representing each category.

As an ongoing project, each student could continue to collect items and compile individual ephemera scrapbooks throughout the school year.

Scrapbooking Through the Centuries

1. Go to *Emergence of Advertising in America 1850–1920.*

   http://memory.loc.gov/ammem/award98/ncdhtml/eaahome.html

2. Select "Advertising Categories and Collections."

3. Choose "Scrapbooks" and read the background information about scrapbooks.

4. Answer these questions.

   What is the definition of the word "scrapbook?"_____

   _____

   When did creating scrapbooks become a popular hobby? _____

   _____

   What kinds of items did people put in early scrapbooks?_____

   _____

   _____

   What happened to most old scrapbooks? _____

   _____

5. What items are included in your family scrapbooks? _____

   _____

   _____

Explore a 19th Century Scrapbook!

1. Go to *Emergence of Advertising in America 1850–1920.*

   http://memory.loc.gov/ammem/award98/ncdhtml/eaahome.html

2. Select "Advertising Categories and Collections."

3. Choose "Scrapbooks."

4. Go to the "Browse the Scrapbooks Category" at the top of the page.

5. Explore one of the four online scrapbooks by clicking on the scrapbook title and exploring the pages. Pages can be enlarged for detailed observation.

6. List the types of items and images in this scrapbook.

   _____

   _____

   _____

7. What did you learn about the person who made the scrapbook?

   _____

   _____

   _____

   _____

8. What did you learn about the time period in which the scrapbook was created?

   _____

   _____

   _____

   _____

Famous Faces

Creative Americans
Portraits by
Carl Van Vechten
1932 - 1964

21.2 Prints and Photographs Division, Library of Congress

Students learn about famous Americans and their relationship to the historical, artistic, cultural, scientific, and political backgrounds in which they lived.

American Variety Stage: Vaudeville and Popular Entertainment 1870–1920

This multimedia anthology features movies, playbills, sound recordings, play scripts, and photos documenting popular forms of early entertainment.

http://memory.loc.gov/ammem/vshtml/vshome.html

Creative Americans: Portraits by Carl Van Vechten 1932–1964

Most of the 1,395 photos in this collection feature portrait photographs of celebrities.

http://memory.loc.gov/ammem/vvhtml/vvhome.html

Famous People: Selected Portraits from the Collections of the Library of Congress

This alphabetically organized list links to hundreds of portraits of men and women of all nationalities and from all time periods.

http://lcweb.loc.gov/rr/print/235_alph.html

Houdini: A Biographical Chronology
http://memory.loc.gov/ammem/vshtml/vshchrn.html

Activities:

★ *Famous Faces Portrait Gallery*

Give each student a copy of the activity page.

Students will need colorful paper, scissors, and glue for mounting the selected photos.

Selections could be limited to specific categories to tie in with units on specific subjects (scientists, African Americans, explorers, presidents, women, etc.).

Create a classroom "Famous Faces" gallery (or three-ring binder) and add to this collection throughout the year.

★ *A Houdini Biopoem*

Give each student a copy of the activity page.

Post photos and poems in your "Famous Faces" gallery and/or publish a "Houdini Biopoem" collection online or in print.

Hold short poetry reading sessions to give students an opportunity to share their poems with the group.

★ *Meet Creative Americans*

Before students begin the activity, brainstorm the concept of creativity with the class. Who can be classified as creative? Can creativity be measured?

Give each student a copy of the activity page.

Students will need colorful paper, scissors, and glue for mounting the selected photos.

Post photos and essays in your "Famous Faces" gallery in a special section titled "Creative Americans."

★ *Famous Faces Quotations*

Give each student a copy of the activity page, scissors, and a sheet of colored paper.

Add photos with quotations to your "Famous Faces" gallery.

Famous Faces Portrait Gallery

1. Go to *Famous People: Selected Portraits from the Collections of the Library of Congress*.

   http://lcweb.loc.gov/rr/print/235_alph.html

2. Browse the list and select someone who interests you.

3. Click on the photo of the selected person to enlarge it.

4. Print a copy of the photo and mount it on colorful paper.

5. Write the name of the person below the photo on the colored paper.

6. Use reference materials online or at your library to locate information about the person.

7. As you research this person, write short answers to these questions.

   When did this person live?

   Where did this person live and work as an adult?

   Why is this person famous?

   Why did you select this person?

   What did you learn about life in the U.S. at the time this person lived?

8. On another sheet of paper, write a paragraph to summarize what you learned.

A Houdini Biopoem

1. Go to *Houdini: A Biographical Chronology.*

http://memory.loc.gov/ammem/vshtml/vshchrn.html

2. Read about Houdini's life. Link to copies of Houdini photos and memorabilia.

3. Select and print an interesting photo or document from the collection.

4. A biopoem is a poem about a specific person. Use this pattern to create a biopoem about Harry Houdini.

Line 1: First name.
Line 2: Four adjectives describing his character.
Line 3: Who was... (3–4 words describing his career)
Line 4: Who loves... (3 things)
Line 5: Who feels... (3 things)
Line 6: Who needs... (3 things)
Line 7: Who gives... (3 things)
Line 8: Who fears... (3 things)
Line 9: Who believes...
Line 10: Who lived...
Line 11: Last name.

5. Write the first drafts of your biopoem on scrap paper. Polish and edit it.

6. When you finish, rewrite your poem neatly on fancy paper.

Don't forget to title your poem.

Name _____ Date _____

Meet Creative Americans

1. Write your personal definition of a creative person.

2. Go to *Creative Americans: Portraits by Carl Van Vechten 1932–1964.*

   http://memory.loc.gov/ammem/vvhtml/vvhome.html

3. Browse the "Occupations Index" to explore the categories.

4. List five occupations included in this collection._____

   _____

   _____

5. Browse the list and select someone from a field that interests you.

6. Click on the photo of the selected person to enlarge it.

7. Print a copy of the photo and mount it on colorful paper.

8. Use reference materials online or at your library to locate information about the person.

9. On another sheet of paper, write a two- or three-paragraph essay that answers the following questions:

   What creative contributions did this person make to his/her field?

   Why did you choose this person for further study?

   How does this compare with your definition of a creative person?

Famous Faces Quotations

1. Go to *Famous People: Selected Portraits from the Collections of the Library of Congress.*

   http://lcweb.loc.gov/rr/print/235_alph.html

2. Browse the list and select someone who interests you.

3. Click on the photo of the selected person to enlarge it.

4. Print a copy of the photo and mount it on colorful paper.

5. Use online search engines or print resources to locate a quotation by that person.

6. Write the quote in the speech bubble below and cut it out.

7. Glue the speech bubble to the photo to make it look like the person is saying those words.

8. On the back of the photo, list the person's name, occupation, dates of birth and death, the historical significance of the quotation, and the time, place, and/or source of the quotation.

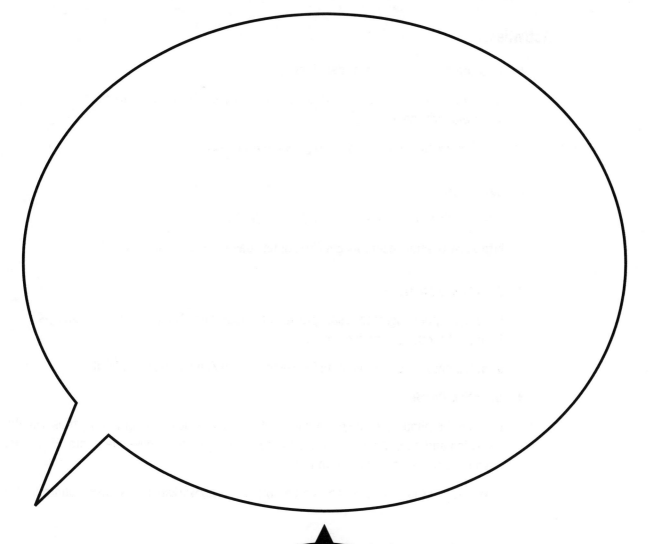

83

Games Galore

22.1

22.2

Students have fun exploring American Memory primary sources through these ready-to-go online games.

Activities:

★ *Amazing Americans Scavenger Hunt*

Find pictures of the items on the Scavenger Hunt list. All the pictures have something to do with presidents.

http://www.americaslibrary.gov/cgi-bin/hunt.cgi/aa

★ *Batter Up!*

This question and answer game highlights the history of baseball.

http://www.americaslibrary.gov/jp/games/baseball/baseball_game.html

★ *Big Picture Puzzles*

Have fun putting together jigsaw puzzle sets made from American Memory images. Then hunt for the theme for each set.

http://memory.loc.gov/ammem/ndlpedu/activity/puzzle/puzintro.html

★ *Counting Puzzle*

Click on the photo to enlarge it. Print it out onto cardstock and cut it into strips. Number the strips and have students put the photo back together. Discuss the photo. Find other interesting photos to make more puzzles.

http://lcweb2.loc.gov/ammem/ndlpedu/educators/workshop/discover/countpuz.html

★ *Historical Detective*

Search the American Memory collection to solve a historical riddle. Find more mysteries by checking the archive.

http://memory.loc.gov/ammem/ndlpedu/features/detect/detectiv.html

★ *Matching Page*

Print this page and match photos illustrating the same task. Discuss how families accomplish these tasks today.

http://memory.loc.gov/ammem/ndlpedu/educators/workshop/discover/matchup.html

★ *Port of Entry*

Use investigative skills to learn about immigrant life in America.

http://memory.loc.gov/ammem/ndlpedu/features/port/start.html

★ *States Treasure Hunt*

Find pictures of the items on the Treasure Hunt list. All of the pictures are in the Explore the States stories and have something to do with food.

http://www.americaslibrary.gov/cgi-bin/hunt.cgi/es

★ *Super Sleuth Game*

Find something that doesn't fit into the time period of each photograph.

http://www.americaslibrary.gov/game/jb/sleuth_intro.html

★ *Who's That Lady?*

Play an online "bowl" type game featuring first lady facts.

http://memory.loc.gov/ammem/ndlpedu/features/lady/index.html

Holidays and Seasonal Celebrations

TEACHER PAGE

Students examine primary documents related to holidays, celebrations, and special events through the school year.

Today in History

This American Memory feature provides a thematic page for each day with links to related documents throughout the collections

http://memory.loc.gov/ammem/today/today.html

Activities:

★ *Celebrate EVERY Day!*

Give each student a copy of the activity page.

You could assign each student a different day of the month. When students finish, write the names of the holidays they created on a class calendar.

Each day, ask the student who created the "new" holiday for that day to give a brief presentation about the day's events to the class.

★ *Thanksgiving Celebrations*

As a tie-in with a unit on Thanksgiving, students can view the American Memory feature presentation *Thanksgiving in American Memory* for a thorough history of this traditional American celebration.

The online Thanksgiving Timeline features documents and photographs from 1541 to 2001.

http://memory.loc.gov/ammem/ndlpedu/features/thanks/thanks.html

★ *Cemetery Sleuthing*

What better way to celebrate Halloween than by exploring a cemetery? Cemeteries are filled with history, so this activity could be used any time of the year.

Search the American Memory collection using keywords such as tombstones, monuments, cemeteries, gravestones, funerals, and other related terms.

These links will take you to some of the many fascinating photographs that can be found throughout the collections:

★ *Grave scaffold:*

http://memory.loc.gov/cgi-bin/query/r?ammem/hawp:@field
(NUMBER+@band(codhawp+10031280))

★ *Haida grave marker:*

http://memory.loc.gov/cgi-bin/query/r?ammem/aipn:@field(DOCID+@lit(p1765))

★ *Beatrice Houdini and Theodore Hardeen visit Houdini's grave:*

http://memory.loc.gov/cgi-bin/query/r?ammem/varstg:@field
(NUMBER+@band(varshoud+3c12441))

★ *Gravestone of the first man killed in the Revolutionary War:*

http://lcweb2.loc.gov/cgi-bin/query/r?ammem/detr:@field(NUMBER+@band
(det+4a22313))

★ *Roosevelt's funeral procession with horse-drawn casket:*

http://memory.loc.gov/cgi-bin/query/r?ammem/presp:@field
(NUMBER+@band(cph+3b14914))

★ *Grave of Kit Carson:*

http://memory.loc.gov/cgi-bin/query/r?ammem/hawp:@field
(NUMBER+@band(codhawp+00170227))

Print the photos and include descriptive information on the back of the photos. Number the photos and place in numerical order around a table or on a wall.

Create a worksheet with scavenger hunt questions based on the photos that can be answered by examining the photos and/or the descriptive information about the photos.

★ *Questions might include:*

Whose funeral is shown on photo 1?

Where is the cemetery in photo 2 located?

When was photo 3 taken?

According to the grave marker on photo 4, how old was the person when he/she died?

Which photo shows a grave marker in the shape of a bear?

Have students fill in answers by examining the photos and reading descriptions.

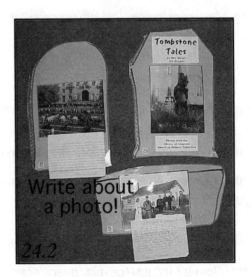

★ *Tombstone Tales*

Give each student a copy of the activity page and the Primary Resource Companion on page 6.

Create a "wall cemetery." Cut out large gray tombstones in different shapes. Display photos and student writing on the paper tombstones. Display in the classroom or hall.

★ *Winter Fun*

Mount all photos in a bulletin board collage using the descriptive words to create a border around the outside of the display. Intersperse paper snowflakes between the words.

Celebrate EVERY Day!

1. Go to *Today in History.*

   http://memory.loc.gov/ammem/today/today.html

2. Click on "Today in History" to find photos, documents, audio files, and movie files related to today.

3. From the archive page, select your birthday or any day of the year. If you have been assigned a specific day, go to that day.

   http://memory.loc.gov/ammem/today/archive.html

4. Read about events for that day.

5. Select one event people could celebrate.

   Example: On May 1, 1931 President Herbert Hoover officially opened the Empire State building to the public.

   People could celebrate Empire State Building Day on May 1.

   What event did you select?_____

   _____

   Who was involved? _____

   When did it occur?_____

   Why was it important? _____

   _____

   What would you name your holiday? _____

   List three ways people could celebrate this holiday. _____

   _____

   _____

   _____

You can search the archive to find a specific holiday. Columbus Day, Thanksgiving, Earth Day, Easter, Spring, April Fool's Day, Veterans Day, Christmas, and Memorial Day are only a few of the many special days featured.

Tombstone Tales

1. Select one photo from the Cemetery Sleuth collection provided by your teacher.

2. Analyze the photo by completing the Primary Resource Organizer.

3. Imagine you are actually observing this scene in person.

   Write a paragraph describing what you see. Include answers to these questions:

   What do you know about the photo?

   How do you feel about the scene?

   What do you wonder about the scene?

Name _____   Date _____

Winter Fun

How did people travel, work, or play in winters past? Collecting photos to illustrate winter life can be entertaining and informative.

As a group:

1. Brainstorm winter words you could use to search the American Memory collection for photos of winter fun.

On your own:

2. Go to the *American Memory* search page.

http://memory.loc.gov/ammem/mdbquery.html

3. Search the collection using words from the brainstormed list. Limit your search to photos and prints.

4. Find and print two or three photos you like.

5. Label each photo with the title, date, and collection.

6. Study the photos carefully. List at least three descriptive winter words for each photo.

Photo 1: _____

Photo 2: _____

Photo 3: _____

7. Use a computer to enlarge and print the descriptive words using a large size font. Cut the words apart and glue them at different angles to your photos.

Immigrating to America

25.1

25.3

Students learn about immigration to the U.S. by examining primary sources.

Selected Images of Ellis Island and Immigration, ca. 1880–1920

A research aid compiled by the Prints and Photographs Division.

http://lcweb.loc.gov/rr/print/070_immi.html

Selected Views of the Statue of Liberty

A research aid compiled by the Prints and Photographs Division.

http://lcweb.loc.gov/rr/print/077_stat.html

Activities:

★ *Port of Entry: Immigration*

Visit this online lesson as a group. Have students become "historical detectives" to uncover stories of immigrants to the United States.

http://memory.loc.gov/ammem/ndlpedu/features/port/start.html

★ *From an Immigrant's Point of View*

Give each student a copy of the activity page.

Display photos and first person essays in a class scrapbook.

★ *Where Did They Come From?*

Print the first three pages of the document *Immigration Figures for 1903*. Make copies for each student.

http://memory.loc.gov/cgi-bin/query/r?ammem/rbpebib:@field (NUMBER+@band(rbpe+07902500))

Give each student a copy of the activity page.

Ask students to look at the second paragraph of the "General Remarks" section and point out the statement which shows prejudice.

Today, Commissioner Williams' statements would be unacceptable to most people, but in 1903, they were quite common.

Discuss how prejudice and discrimination have changed since 1903.

Answers:
1. 857,046
2. Southern Italy, Poland, Scandinavia
3. 1900
4. 1902
5. b
6. United Kingdom, France, Germany, Scandinavia, Belgium, Netherlands, Switzerland
7. $19
8. 9,316
9. People over 14 who cannot write or cannot read and write their own language.
10. 189,008
11. See document.
12. Answers will vary.
13. at least 200,000

Where Did They Come From?

Use the primary source *Immigration Figures for 1903* to answer the questions.

1. How many immigrants entered the U.S. in 1903? _____

2. From what three areas did the most immigrants arrive in 1903? _____

   _____

   _____

3. In which year (1899, 1900, 1901, 1902, 1903) did the most Irish immigrants arrive? _____

4. In which year (1899, 1900, 1901, 1902, 1903) did the most Slovak immigrants arrive? _____

5. From which region did the most immigrants arrive in 1903?

   a. Northern and Western Europe
   b. Southern and Eastern Europe
   c. Asia

6. What countries were included in the category "Northern and Western Europe?" _____

   _____

7. How much money did the average immigrant bring to the U.S. in 1903? _____

8. In 1903, how many immigrants were debarred (turned away) or returned within one year?_____

9. According to the document, what does illiterate mean? _____

   _____

   _____

10. How many of the 1903 immigrants were illiterate?_____

11. The Hon. William Williams, Commissioner of New York, listed seven reasons why immigrants were "generally undesirable." Find that passage in the document and underline it.

12. Do you think his reasons are good ones? Why or why not?_____

    _____

    _____

    _____

    _____

13. How many "undesirable" immigrants did Williams feel had entered the country in 1903?_____

From An Immigrant's Point of View

25.1

1. Go to *Selected Images of Ellis Island and Immigration, ca. 1880–1920.*

   http://lcweb.loc.gov/rr/print/070_immi.html

2. Click on each photo to enlarge it. Click on the text below the photo to read details about the image.

3. Select and print one photograph that includes people.

4. Imagine being one of the people in the photograph. Circle that person.

5. On another sheet of paper, write an essay about your early impression of America from this person's point of view using clues from the photograph.

   Hints:

   Study the person's expression. Try to understand how he or she felt when the photo was taken.

   Examine what the person is wearing. What does that tell you about the social or financial situation of the person?

   Observe other people in the group. How are they related? How are they interacting with your person?

   Examine details of the place where the photo was taken. Describe the sights, sounds, and smells around your person.

Marvelous Maps

27.2

Students explore primary source maps in the Library of Congress collections.

Map Collections: 1500–Present

This online map collection represents only a small fraction of the 4.5 million maps in the Library of Congress Geography and Map Division's holdings. Students can zoom in on sections of the map to see more detail.

http://memory.loc.gov/ammem/gmdhtml/gmdhome.html

The National Atlas of the United States, Washington, 1970

This online atlas contains hundreds of United States maps featuring historical, economic, geologic, and physical data.

http://memory.loc.gov/cgi-bin/query/r?ammem/gmd:@field
(NUMBER+@band(g3701gm+gct00013))

Activities:

★ *Map Sampler*

Give each student a copy of the activity page.

This activity can be done as a group or individually. If done as a group, select maps for viewing in advance.

Suggestions for fascinating maps in each category include:

★ *Cities and Towns:*
Grand birds' eye view of the Great East River Suspension Bridge connecting the cities of New York and Brooklyn and showing the splendid panorama of the bay and part of New York. (Currier and Ives, c.1885)
http://memory.loc.gov/cgi-bin/query/r?ammem/gmd:@field
(NUMBER+@band(g3804n+pm006021))

★ *Conservation and Environment:*
Map of the northeast coast of North America, 1607, drawn by Samuel de Champlain: a facsimile from the Library of Congress.
http://lcweb2.loc.gov/cgi-bin/query/r?ammem/gmd:@field
(NUMBER+@band(g3321p+np000002))

★ *Discovery and Exploration:*
Map of California shown as an island. (1650)
http://lcweb2.loc.gov/cgi-bin/query/r?ammem/gmd:@field
(NUMBER+@band(g3291s+mf000074))

★ *Cultural Landscapes:*
A plan of my farm on Little Huntg. Creek and Potomk. (George Washington, 1766)
http://lcweb2.loc.gov/cgi-bin/query/r?ammem/gmd:@field
(NUMBER+@band(g3882m+ct000085))

★ *Military Battles and Campaigns:*
A plan of the town of Boston and its environs with the lines, batteries, and encampments of the British and American Armies. (1776)
http://lcweb2.loc.gov/cgi-bin/query/r?ammem/gmd:@field
(NUMBER+@band(g3764b+ct000252))

★ *Transportation and Communication:*
Oregon Trail map with notes by John Fremont. (1846)
http://lcweb2.loc.gov/cgi-bin/query/r?ammem/gmd:@field
(NUMBER+@band(g4127o+mf000054))

★ *General Maps:*
North America divided into its three principal parts. (1685)
http://memory.loc.gov/cgi-bin/query/r?ammem/gmd:@field
(NUMBER+@band(g3300+mf000041))

★ *Places in the News*

Have students look at the front page of several current newspapers and list several countries that are currently "in the news."

As a group, visit **Places in the News**, an online presentation from the LOC Geography and Map Division featuring maps related to current news events.

http://memory.loc.gov/ammem/gmdhtml/plnews.html

Read country information and explore the map with the students. Is the featured country one of the ones they listed? What can they learn about why it is "in the news?" If not, why is that country featured?

★ *Zoom into the National Atlas*

Give each student a copy of the activity page.

Once students feel comfortable using the zoom tool, they can find hundreds of fascinating U.S. maps in the atlas to visit. Show them how to use the "Next Group" button to move through the pages to explore samples:

> Image 58—Glacial Geology
> Image 85—Air Pollution
> Image 97—Indian Tribes, Cultures and Languages
> Image 106—Historic Sites and Landmarks

This atlas can serve as a useful online reference tool throughout the year.

★ *YOUR City in Panoramic View*

Share the information about the history of panoramic mapping with students before they begin this activity.

The Panoramic Map collection includes wonderful 19th century maps of urban areas. Although not always drawn to scale, they show street patterns, individual buildings, and major landscape features in perspective.

Give each student a copy of the activity page.

Provide a current city map for comparison.

Students can print enlarged sections of the map to use in conjunction with a hometown walking tour.

Map Sampler

1. Go to *Map Collections: 1500–Present.*

http://memory.loc.gov/ammem/gmdhtml/gmdhome.html

2. Explore at least one map from each of the seven categories.

Write the name of each map and one comment about what you observed about that map.

Cities and Towns: _____

_____

_____

Conservation and Environment: _____

_____

_____

Discovery and Exploration: _____

_____

_____

Cultural Landscapes: _____

_____

_____

Military Battles and Campaigns: _____

_____

_____

Transportation and Communication: _____

_____

_____

General Maps: _____

_____

_____

Let's Compare

27.2

1. Go to *Map Collections: 1500–Present.*

   http://memory.loc.gov/ammem/gmdhtml/gmdhome.html

2. Select and print one map from two different categories.

3. Write the title and date on the back of each map.

4. Study the maps for details.

5. List ways the two maps are similar: _____

   _____

   _____

   _____

   _____

   _____

   _____

6. List ways the two maps are different: _____

   _____

   _____

   _____

   _____

   _____

   _____

   _____

Zoom into the National Atlas

1. Go to *Map Collections: 1500–Present.*

http://memory.loc.gov/ammem/gmdhtml/gmdhome.html

2. Click on "Search by Keyword" and type in "National Atlas of the United States."

3. Click the title to go to the atlas.

4. Click on the book image to see thumbnail views of all online pages.

5. Use the zoom tool to explore the first three pages and answer these questions.

When and where was the atlas published? _____

Who was the atlas dedicated to? _____

Who was president at the time? _____

What animal is pictured on the frontispiece? _____

What is the date under the animal? _____

What organization is named above the image? _____

6. Click on "Next Group" at the bottom of the page. Select the regional map that features your state.

7. Zoom in until you locate the city where you live. Print a copy of this map section.

8. Explore the map. List details you recognize about your city._____

_____

_____

_____

_____

YOUR City in Panoramic View

1. Go to *Map Collections: 1500–Present.*

   http://memory.loc.gov/ammem/gmdhtml/gmdhome.html

2. Go to the "Cities and Towns" collection.

3. Scroll down this page and go to the "Panoramic Maps Collection."

4. Browse the panoramic maps collection by Geographic Location.

5. Click on your state and browse the cities and towns listed.

6. Select a map of your city. If your city is not listed, select a city nearby.

7. Use the zoom feature to explore the map in detail.

   What familiar street names can you find? _____

   _____

   What familiar buildings can you find? _____

   _____

   What local land features (mountains, rivers, valleys, etc.) can you find? _____

   _____

8. Compare this map with a current map of your city.

   How has your city changed? _____

   _____

   _____

   _____

   _____

Math in American Memory

I spy shapes and numbers in American Memory photos! Can you?

28.1

Students locate and analyze American Memory documents from a mathematical perspective.

Taking the Long View: Panoramic Photographs 1851–1991

This collection contains approximately 4,000 images featuring American cityscapes, landscapes, and group portraits.

http://memory.loc.gov/ammem/pnhtml/pnhome.html

Activities:

★ *"I Spy" Math*

Brainstorm mathematical terms with the class. Write the list on the board or chart paper.

Encourage students to think about words describing shapes (octagon, triangle, pentagon, cylinder, square), large numbers (million, thousand), measurement devices (abacus, ruler, scale, calculator), and mathematical terms (intersect, parallel, circumference, diameter).

Assign two to four mathematical terms to each student.

Give each student a copy of the activity page.

Students will need colored construction paper, scissors, and glue.

Display the mounted photos on a bulletin board or along a hallway.

Give the class a few minutes to study the display. Have each student read his or her "I Spy" questions, one at a time.

Members of the class try to be the first to find the image that matches.

★ **Keeping Track**

Give each student a copy of the activity page.

Encourage students to find and explore similar documents.

★ **Create a Counting Book**

Divide students into groups.

Give each student a copy of the activity page.

Have each group compile their counting book in a three-ring report cover. If possible, laminate the pages or insert them in plastic page protectors for durability.

Make arrangements with a teacher from a preschool, kindergarten, or first grade class for your students to share their counting books with small groups of children.

Donate the counting books to a preschool, kindergarten, or first grade class.

★ **Panoramic Puzzles**

Have students locate interesting photos from the site *Taking the Long View: Panoramic Photographs 1851–1991.*

http://memory.loc.gov/ammem/pnhtml/pnhome.html

Students can print the photos on cardstock and laminate them. Have them cut the photograph into interesting geometric shapes.

Students can put puzzle pieces in an envelope and label it with the title of the photograph.

Let each student select a classmate's puzzle and make it.

Students can take their puzzles home to share with their families.

"I Spy" Math

1. Go to the *American Memory* search page.

   http://memory.loc.gov/ammem/mdbquery.html

2. Search the collection using the assigned math terms as keywords (cube, triangle, diameter, parallel, etc.). Limit your search to photos and prints.

3. Locate and print images for each math term.

4. Mount your images on colored construction paper.

5. Write the image title and summary on the back of the construction paper.

6. Create an "I Spy" question for each photo.

I spy _____

_____

I spy _____

_____

I spy _____

_____

I spy _____

_____

Keeping Track

1. Go to the *American Memory* search page.

http://memory.loc.gov/ammem/mdbquery.html

2. Find these historical documents related to money and spending. See how costs have changed over time.

3. Search using the keywords "account book." Examine the Morrison (Ship) Account Book kept by Samuel Green from 1844 to 1846 on a voyage to the Pacific Ocean whaling grounds.

Go to image 4. List 5 items the captain purchased. _____

_____

_____

4. George Washington was careful with his money. Search using the keywords "cash memorandum" to learn how he spent his money. Examine his 1774–1775 "Pocket Day Book."

Scroll through the pages in the book by clicking on "Next Image." Find a page that lists expenses.

What are five items George Washington listed as expenses?_____

_____

_____

5. Running the government is expensive. Search using the keyword "budget" to find Thomas Jefferson's 1777 list of expenses for the Continental Congress.

What was the amount listed for November 29, 1775? _____

6. Prices are on the rise. Search using the keywords "price list" to view prices from long ago.

Find and print Persons' New Price List.

Prices at Persons' store in Boston in 1861 seem pretty reasonable to us today. Select three items from the list that are similar to things people could still buy today.

Complete the chart.

Item from Persons' Store	Cost in 1861	Cost Today
_____	_____	_____
_____	_____	_____
_____	_____	_____

Create a Counting Book

Counting books help young children read and understand numbers and see the relationship between abstract numbers and the real world.

As a group:

1. Decide on what numbers to cover in your counting book and who will find the material for each number. Suggestions include: 1 to 10, 1 to 12, 1 to 20, 5 to 50 by fives, or 10 to 100 by tens.

On your own:

2. Go to the *American Memory* search page.

http://memory.loc.gov/ammem/mdbquery.html

3. Search the collection using numbers as keywords for your assigned numbers. Limit your search to photos and prints.

4. Select interesting photos to represent each number.

5. Print the photos. Include descriptive information about the photo on the back.

6. On colored paper, write the number and a short sentence about the picture. See sample below.

Use colorful markers or create your pages on the computer using large, fun fonts.

As a group:

7. Arrange the written pages and photos so the ones that go together are on facing pages. Compile your book in a three-ring report cover.

Three ships sailing across the sea.

8. Share your counting book with students from a lower grade.

Newscasts From the Past

10.1

Students create a "news broadcast" to narrate while classmates view the film.

Activity:

★ *You Are There*

Imagine "being there" during a great historic event. Many American Memory collections feature motion pictures, most of which contain no narration. These provide excellent footage for students to research and write narration.

To locate suitable motion pictures, go to the "Collection Finder" page and select "motion pictures."

http://memory.loc.gov/ammem/collections/finder.html

This links to a list of all motion picture film collections. Films include over 300 of Thomas Edison's early films, Westinghouse Factory films from the early 1900s, San Francisco and 1906 Earthquake films, Presidential Inaugurations, over 100 Theodore Roosevelt films, Spanish American War films, films from early New York City life, and many others.

Divide students into small groups to create a narrative to accompany a motion picture in the LOC collection.

Select a collection that ties in with historical content being covered in class.

You can use the suggestions at the end of this section or select titles that fit your curriculum.

Assign a film clip from that collection to each group or allow groups to select their own.

Download and save the clips to the computer for easier access.

Have students develop a narrative that covers the who, what, when, where, and why of the event. The narrative should be written so viewers feel that the historic moments being shown are breaking news.

If narration accompanies the film, turn down the sound so the student's own words will be heard.

Suggestions:

★ *Emigrants Landing at Ellis Island* from Life of a City Collection.

http://memory.loc.gov/cgibin/query/r?ammem/papr:@filreq(@field (NUMBER+@band(lcmp002+m2a10987))+@field(COLLID+newyork))

★ *Loading Baggage for the Klondike* from Inventing Entertainment, 1897–1920.

http://memory.loc.gov/cgi-bin/query/r?ammem/papr:@field(NUMBER+@band (edmp+0017))

★ *San Francisco earthquake and fire, April 8, 1906* from Before and After the Great Earthquake and Fire: Early Films of San Francisco, 1897–1916.

http://memory.loc.gov/cgibin/query/r?ammem/papr:@field(NUMBER+@band (lcmp003+03734s4))

Additional Resource:

★ *We Interrupt This Broadcast: Relive the Events that Stopped Our Lives* by Joe Garner; foreword by Walter Cronkite; narrated by Bill Kurtis. (Sourcebooks Inc., 2000) This book and accompanying audio CD-ROMs could be used as a model or supplement for this activity.

Photo Fun

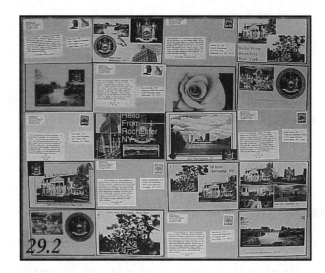

29.2

These activities can be used in conjunction with photo analysis projects across the curriculum.

America's First Look into the Camera: Daguerreotype Portraits and Views, 1839–1864

This collection features 725 photographs dating from 1839 to 1864.

http://memory.loc.gov/ammem/daghtml/daghome.html

Activities:

★ *Postcards from the Past*

Assign themes/topics for student postcards related to your current curriculum. Topics could include a specific time period, location, or broad subject such as transportation.

Give each student a copy of the activity page.

They will also need cardstock and glue.

Students may need help resizing images to fit the 4" x 6" format. They could transfer the image to an appropriate software program to resize, enhance, and/or crop the image.

Postcards can be mailed, displayed, or collected in a class scrapbook.

★ *Pet Parade*

Before students begin, locate and print several pet photos as examples. Some interesting ones include:

Alligator Joe and His Pets:
http://memory.loc.gov/cgi-bin/query/r?ammem/detr:@field
(NUMBER+@band(det+4a11872))

Mrs. Coolidge with her pet raccoon, Rebecca:
http://memory.loc.gov/cgi-bin/query/r?ammem/coolbib:@field
(NUMBER+@band(cph+3b39483))

Cat with a pet rat:
http://memory.loc.gov/cgi-bin/query/r?ammem/hawp:@field
(NUMBER+@band(codhawp+00189487))

Give each student a copy of the activity page.

When they finish, have students cut the activity page, saving only their paragraphs.

Display the photos and student writing, gallery style, along a wall in the classroom or hall.

The poster "Pet Show" from the By the People, For the People: Posters from the WPA, 1936–1943 collection can be used to introduce the pet parade.

http://memory.loc.gov/cgi-bin/query/r?ammem/wpapos:@field
(NUMBER+@band(cph+3b48887))

★ *Photo Story Starters*

Select and print interesting photos from the American Memory collection. Photos could all come from one collection and relate to a single theme, or they could be selected from many collections. Photos could be ones printed earlier for other activities. Provide enough photos for each student to have a different one.

Give each student a copy of the activity page.

Create a bulletin board featuring photos and stories.

★ *Daguerreotype Look-Alikes*

Give each student a copy of the activity page.

After students complete the activity, discuss these questions.

How are daguerreotype photos different than ones taken today?

How are daguerreotype photos similar to formal portrait photos taken today?

How has technology made a difference in photography?

★ *Create a Student Daguerreotype Gallery*

With a digital camera, have students take portrait photos of each other posing "daguerreotype-style."

Download the photos to your computer. Using appropriate software, students can change the photos of themselves to black and white or sepia tone.

Have students print the photos and mount on colored construction paper or create a daguerreotype-style frame using a large black rectangle for the bottom and a smaller red rectangle on top to create a border.

Insert the photo and cover with an oval or fancy-shaped mat cut out from yellow or gold paper.

Hang portraits in a "Student Daguerreotype Gallery" in the classroom or hall.

Students can take home their daguerreotypes to share with their families or give them to a parent or relative as a gift. (Great Mother's Day or Grandparent's Day gift idea!)

Postcards from the Past

1. Go to the *American Memory* search page.

   http://memory.loc.gov/ammem/mdbquery.html

2. Search the collection using keywords related to the assigned topic. Limit your search to photos and prints.

3. Select a photo you could use to create a "postcard from the past."

4. Resize the photo so the image is no more than 4" by 6".

5. Print the image on card stock and cut to size (or print and glue to a piece of 4" x 6" cardstock).

6. Add other graphics or clip art if desired.

7. Divide the back of the card in half.

8. On the right half, address the postcard to someone you know. Leave room to add a stamp in the top right corner.

9. In the top left corner, write a short caption for the postcard.

10. Below the caption, write a message to person who will receive the card.

caption here

stamp

your message here

TO:

_____

_____

_____

_____

Pet Parade

1. Go to the *American Memory* search page.

   http://memory.loc.gov/ammem/mdbquery.html

2. Search the collection using the keyword "pets." Limit your search to photos and prints.

3. Browse through several of the photos you found.

4. Select and print a photo showing someone with a pet that you think is interesting or funny.

5. Imagine being the person shown in the photograph and that the pet shown is actually yours.

   Write a paragraph about "your" pet from this person's point of view. Use clues in the photograph including the setting, the expression on the person's face, the pose of the person and the pet, and other items shown in the photo.

   _____

   _____

   _____

   _____

   _____

   _____

   _____

   _____

   _____

   _____

   _____

   _____

   _____

   _____

   _____

   _____

   _____

   _____

   _____

   _____

Photo Story Starters

1. Select one of the photos provided by your teacher to use to write a short story.

2. Examine the photo closely. As you answer these questions, make notes to use in your story.

    Which person in the photo will be the main character of your story?

    What will your main character's name be?

    About how old is the person?

    What can you learn about the person from the types of shoes, clothing, jewelry, hat, or other items he or she is wearing?

    What can you learn about the person's hobbies or type of work he or she may do for a living?

    What can you learn about the person's personality from the expression on his or her face?

    What visual clues tell you about when and where the photo might have been taken?

    What will be the setting for your story?

    What might have happened minutes before the photo was taken?

    What happened after the photo was taken?

Most stories involve some type of conflict or problem between the main character and another person, the main character and nature, or the main character and an event. What type of conflict could you include in your story?

How could your character solve the problem?

3. On another sheet of paper, write a short story based on the photo and your notes.

4. Polish and rewrite your story. Edit and proofread it. Add a title.

Name _____ Date _____

Daguerreotype Look-Alikes

1. Go to *America's First Look into the Camera: Daguerreotype Portraits and Views, 1839–1864.*

   http://memory.loc.gov/ammem/daghtml/daghome.html

2. Browse through the collection.

3. Select and print one photograph of a boy or girl about your age. If possible, find one that looks something like you.

4. Answer these questions about the photo.

   What is the person in the photograph doing? _____

   _____

   What kind of clothes is he or she wearing? _____

   _____

   What kinds of props or objects are included in the photos? _____

   _____

   _____

   What expression is on his or her face? _____

   _____

   How does the photo reflect the time period when the photo was taken? _____

   _____

   _____

   What is there about the person that reminds you of yourself? _____

   _____

   _____

Poetry for Pleasure

Poet at Work
Recovered Notebooks from the Thomas Biggs Harned
Walt Whitman Collection

30.1   Manuscript Division, Library of Congress

Students read poetry and use poetic formats to analyze primary documents.

Activities:

★ Poetry in American Memory

Students can go to the American Memory search page and use the keywords poem, poet, or poetry to locate hundreds of poems in the American Memory collection.

http://memory.loc.gov/ammem/mdbquery.html

Have each student select, print, and share a poem with the class.

As a class, discuss the variety of poems that can be found in the collection and what can be learned from each about the historical period during which it was written.

★ A Haiku Nature Photo Poem

Give each student a copy of the activity page.

Post photos and haiku poems in a "Photo Poetry" gallery.

★ Biopoems

Students can write biopoems about people found in the American Memory collection. Use the format from the "A Houdini Biopoem" activity on page 81 of this book.

117

Watt's Divine Songs, New-York Cries,
    And Select Hymns for Youth,
New Riddle Book, and Little Ann,
    A narrative of truth.

New-York Scenes, the Child's First Book,
    Poetic Tales, quite good,
The Blackbird's Nest, the Pious Gift,
    The Children in the Wood.

30.3

★ *Found Poetry in American Memory Documents*

Select a document from the American Memory collection like a letter, speech, diary entry, personal narrative, or other type relating to a topic of current study.

If the document is quite long, like Martin Luther King, Jr.'s "I Have a Dream" speech or the Declaration of Independence, select only a portion of the document to use for this project.

Give each student a copy of the document and the activity page. Students will need construction paper, scissors, and glue.

Read the selection to the class as students follow along. Ask students to highlight or underline words and phrases in the document that appeal to them.

Divide the class into groups to rearrange and combine words and phrases into a new poem.

One member of each group can read the group poem to the class.

For a detailed description of this technique, go to the online lesson *Enhancing a Poetry Unit with American Memory.*

http://memory.loc.gov/ammem/ndlpedu/lessons/98/poetry/poem.html

★ *A-Poem-a-Day the American Memory Way*

Poetry 180: a poem a day for American high schools

http://www.loc.gov/poetry/180/

Visit this terrific American Memory site to make poetry an active part of your students' daily lives. The 180 poems selected by Poet Laureate Billy Collins offer a reading for every day of the school year. Although targeted for high school students, these poems can be read at many grade levels.

For details about implementing the project, click on "more about this program" at the bottom of the page.

For tips on reading poems out loud, click on "how to read a poem out loud" at the bottom of the home page.

For a list of all poems, click on "list of all 180 poems" at the top of the home page.

To read a poem, click on any title in the list or type a poem number in the box.

A Haiku Nature Photo Poem

Haiku is a form of Japanese poetry which uses seventeen syllables in three-line format to create a word picture and mood. Some aspect of nature is often the topic for this type of poetry.

1. Go to the **American Memory** search page.

http://memory.loc.gov/ammem/mdbquery.html

2. Search the collection using keywords related to nature, like summer, winter, hurricane, trees, plants, wild animals, etc. Limit your search to photos and prints.

3. Select and print a photo you like that shows some aspect of nature but does not contain people.

4. Jot down words and phrases about what you see in the photo and how the photo makes you feel.

5. Follow the haiku format to express what you see and feel about the photograph.

Line 1: Five syllables

Line 2: Seven syllables

Line 3: Five syllables

Sample haiku: Hurricane rages,
A wild beast devouring
A path through my life

6. Write your poem on scrap paper. Polish it. Count the number of syllables in each line.

7. Write the final version of your haiku poem here.

_____

_____

_____

Found Poetry In American Memory Documents

A found poem is created by using phrases or words from existing literary work and combining them in new and creative ways.

1. Follow along as your teacher reads the document. Underline words and phrases that appeal to you. Listen for phrases that sound like they might fit into a poem.

2. Look through the words and phrases you underlined. Select four interesting phrases or groups of words.

3. Write one phrase or group of words on each section below.

4. Cut the sections apart.

As a group:

5. Work together to rearrange and combine the words and phrases written by members of the group to create a new poem.

   Each group of words or phrases can be one line of the poem. Words and phrases can be cut apart and combined to make one line. Rearrange the words and phrases until your group is satisfied with the poem.

   Glue the strips of paper to colored construction paper. As a group, decide on a title and write it at the top of the page.

Presidents Past and Present

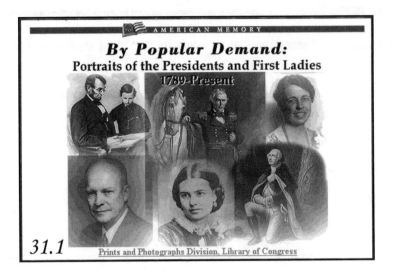

Students explore images and documents in the American Memory collection to learn about United States presidents.

By Popular Demand: Portraits of Presidents and First Ladies
http://memory.loc.gov/ammem/odmdhtml/preshome.html

Activities:

★ *Dynamite Presidents*

http://www.americaslibrary.gov/aa/game/rushmore_noflash.html

Introduce students to an entertaining and thought-provoking question and answer activity about presidents in this America's Library online game.

★ *Elections the American Way*

http://lcweb2.loc.gov/features/election/home.html

As a class or on their own, students can explore the election process, both past and present, in this American Memory online feature presentation. This activity is divided into five sections: candidates, voters, the party system, the election process, and issues.

★ *Inaugurations—From George W. to George W.*

http://memory.loc.gov/ammem/ndlpedu/features/inaug/theatre.html

Students can explore past and present presidential inaugurations in this entertaining American Memory feature presentation. Visit the companion collection, *I Do Solemnly Swear*, for additional documentation and presentations.

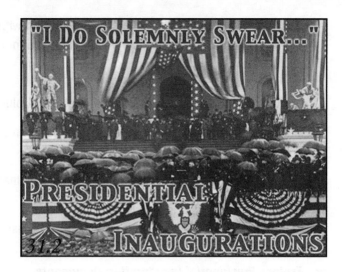

★ *I Do Solemnly Swear*

This collection features items from every presidential inauguration from George Washington's in 1789 to the present, including diaries and letters of presidents and of those who witnessed inaugurations, handwritten drafts of inaugural addresses, broadsides, inaugural tickets and programs, prints, photographs, and sheet music.

http://memory.loc.gov/ammem/pihtml/pihome.html

★ *Presidential Wall of Fame*

This activity could be conducted anytime during the school year, although February (President's Month) or November (Election Month) would be especially appropriate.

Divide the class into small groups by time period with each group responsible for locating and printing photographs of each president in office during that time period.

Give each student a copy of the activity page.

They will need scissors, glue, and red, white, and blue construction paper.

Make a wall collage of presidential pictures and Presidential Facts in a timeline format to create a "Presidential Wall of Fame."

Add items from the activity "Examine Presidential Inauguration Documents" to this display.

Students will use this display to complete the "Presidential Scavenger Hunt" activity.

★ *Explore Presidential Inauguration Documents*

Assign one or more presidents to each student to cover each of the presidents since George Washington. If time is a factor, each student can be assigned to only one president.

Give each student a copy of the activity page and the Primary Resource Companion on page 6. Students researching more than one president will need additional copies of the Presidential Facts form part of the activity page.

Include documents and summaries in your "Presidential Wall of Fame" display.

★ *Presidential Scavenger Hunt*

Give each student a copy of the activity page and a 3" x 5" index card.

Select student questions from the 3" x 5" index cards to read to the group. Have student volunteers answer the questions.

Presidential Wall of Fame

As a group:

1. Go to *By Popular Demand: Portraits of Presidents and First Ladies.*

   http://memory.loc.gov/ammem/odmdhtml/preshome.html

2. Locate and select an image or photograph of each man who was president during the time period assigned to your group.

3. Print the images and mount them on red, white, and/or blue construction paper.

4. Label each image with the president's name and dates of office.

5. Decide who will find additional information about each of the presidents for the time period assigned to your group.

On your own:

6. Use reference materials to learn more about the president(s) assigned to you and complete the Presidential Facts form below.

Name: _____

Date and place of birth: _____

Date and place of death: _____

Political Party: _____

Nickname(s): _____

First lady's name: _____

Children's names: _____

Occupation before becoming president: _____

Favorite hobbies or sports: _____

Two important facts about him while president: _____

_____

_____

_____

_____

_____

_____

125

Examine Presidential Inauguration Documents

1. Go to *I Do Solemnly Swear.*

http://memory.loc.gov/ammem/pihtml/pihome.html

2. Browse the collection for the president(s) assigned to you.

3. Select and print one or more images or documents representing that president's inauguration.

4. Write the name of the president and date of inauguration on the back of each item.

5. Use the Primary Resource Companion to examine each document or photograph.

6. Write a one-paragraph summary of each item.

_____

_____

_____

_____

_____

_____

_____

_____

_____

_____

_____

_____

_____

_____

_____

_____

_____

Presidential Scavenger Hunt

Go to your classroom "Presidential Wall of Fame" display to find the answers to this scavenger hunt.

1. Who is the first president to be pictured with a smile on his face? _____

_____

2. Who is the first president to be pictured with a beard? _____

_____

3. Name the presidents who are pictured wearing glasses. _____

_____

_____

4. Who is the first president to be pictured wearing a necktie? _____

_____

5. Who was the last president to be pictured with either a mustache or beard? _____

_____

6. Which presidents are pictured with the American flag in the background? _____

_____

7. Which presidents have first and last names beginning with the same letter? _____

_____

_____

8. What is the most common first name of all presidents? List the presidents with this first name.

_____

_____

9. Which president served for the longest number of years? _____

_____

10. Which presidents are photographed with books? _____

_____

11. Write your own Presidential Scavenger Hunt question on a 3" x 5" index card. Be sure your question can be answered by examining information on the "Presidential Wall of Fame."

Science Around Us

Students explore science-related primary source documents.

American Environmental Photographs, 1891–1936: Images from the University of Chicago

This collection contains over 4,000 photographs documenting natural environments, ecology, and plant communities in the U.S. at the end of the nineteenth and the beginning of the twentieth century.

http://memory.loc.gov/ammem/award97/icuhtml/aephome.html

North American Animals

This site features an advertising booklet from the Emergence of Advertising in America collection.

http://memory.loc.gov/cgi-bin/query/r?ammem/eaa:@field(DOCID+@lit(A0338))

Activities:

★ *An Earth Science Visual Dictionary*

Before beginning the activity, have the class brainstorm a list of earth science terms. Write the words on the board or chart paper.

A starter list might include: avalanches, basins, boulders, beaches, bridges, canyons, caves, cirque, craters, dams, deltas, deserts, estuaries, fjords, glaciers, gorges, harbors, islands, lakes, ledges, moraines, mountains, peat bogs, sand dunes, and waterfalls.

(Option: create this list in advance to include specific terms you want students to research.)

Assign five earth science terms to each student.

Give each student a copy of the activity page.

Compile the dictionary pages in alphabetical order in a three-ring binder for class use throughout the year.

Option: Create a slide show to share with the class.

★ *North American Animals of the Past*

Before beginning the activity, go to North American Animals.

http://memory.loc.gov/cgi-bin/query/r?ammem/eaa:@field(DOCID+@lit(A0338))

Double click on the cover page to view the booklet. Click on "next" to advance through the pages. For best viewing, enlarge the pages to maximum size.

Print the pages of animals.

Divide the class into groups and give each group one page of animals.

Give each student a copy of the activity page. Students researching more than one animal will need additional copies of the activity page.

★ *Wild and Wooly Weather*

You may want to share the following samples with students before they begin this activity.

The Drought of 1930 and the Flood of 1932

An audio file from the Tending the Commons collection documenting a West Virginia drought and flood.

http://memory.loc.gov/cgi-bin/query/r?ammem/cmns:@field(DOCID+@lit(131003))

The Blizzard of 1888

A personal narrative from the American Life Histories: Manuscripts from the Federal Writers' Project, 1936–1940 collection.

http://memory.loc.gov/cgi-bin/query/r?ammem/wpa:@field (DOCID+@lit(17120802))

Stereoscopic views of the tornado at Wallingford, Connecticut, August 9, 1878

Over 50 views of a destructive tornado from the Small-Town America: Stereoscopic Views from the Robert Dennis Collection, 1850–1920.

http://memory.loc.gov/cgi-bin/query/r?ammem/denn:@field(DOCID+@lit (NYPG90-F64))

Panorama of orphans' home, Galveston

A Thomas Edison film documenting a 1900 cyclone and tidal wave in Galveston, Texas.

http://memory.loc.gov/cgi-bin/query/r?ammem/papr:@field (NUMBER+@band(edmp+1381))

Give each student a copy of the activity sheet and the Question Organizer form on page 7.

Post photos with news articles on a "Wild and Wooly Weather" bulletin board display.

Extension Activity:

Have students type their news articles and headlines, using a larger font for the headlines, and print them from the computer in newspaper column format.

Assign groups of students to prepare "Wild and Wooly Weather" newspaper pages that include the photos of the event, headlines, and news articles.

An Earth Science Visual Dictionary

1. List the earth science terms assigned to you. Use a textbook or encyclopedia to write a short definition for each term.

A. _____

_____

B. _____

_____

C. _____

_____

D. _____

_____

E. _____

_____

2. Go to *American Environmental Photographs, 1891–1936: Images from the University of Chicago*.

http://memory.loc.gov/ammem/award97/icuhtml/aephome.html

3. Use the "search" box to locate and print one photograph that best illustrates each term.

4. Create five pages (one page for each term) for a class Earth Science visual dictionary.

Each page should include:

The term in large letters at the top of the page.
A definition of the term.
A photo that illustrates the term.
The title, date, and source of the photo.

North American Animals of the Past

1. Use reference materials to answer the following questions about the North American animal(s) assigned to you.

   What does the animal look like?

   Where does it live?

   What is its habitat?

   Was this animal of value to early 20th century Americans for fur, food, or other purposes? If yes, list why it was valuable.

   What is its current status? Is the animal threatened, endangered, or extinct today?

2. Cut out the North American Animal Fact Card. Fill in the information. You will need one fact card for each animal.

3. Cut out the picture of the animal. Write the name of the animal on the reverse side of the card and glue a picture of it below its name.

North American Animal Fact Card

Scienific name: _____

Description: _____

_____

_____

Habitat: _____

Habits: _____

_____

_____

Value to Americans: _____

_____

Current Status: _____

_____

Name _____ Date _____

Wild and Wooly Weather

As a group:

1. List words for wild and wooly weather events (blizzards, droughts, floods, etc.)

On your own:

2. Go to the *American Memory* search page.

http://memory.loc.gov/ammem/mdbquery.html

3. Search the collection using one of the weather event words as keywords. Limit your search to photos and prints.

4. Browse through several of the photos you find.

5. Select and print a photo showing wild and wooly weather that you think is interesting.

6. Read and print all information about the photo.

7. Complete the Question Organizer form.

8. Using your answers, write a short news article as though the event had happened only yesterday. Include answers to who, what, when, where, why, and how.

_____

_____

_____

_____

_____

_____

_____

_____

_____

_____

9. A headline summarizes the news event in a few words using active verbs.

Using six words or less, write a headline for your article._____

_____

Songs and Sounds of History

Students learn about America's musical past by exploring the American Memory audio and print resources.

American Variety Stage: Vaudeville and Popular Entertainment 1870–1920

This multimedia anthology highlights popular entertainment of the period.

http://memory.loc.gov/ammem/vshtml/vshome.html

See, Hear, and Sing

An America's Library feature highlighting animation, early movies, and sound and audio files.

http://www.americaslibrary.gov/cgi-bin/page.cgi/sh

Activities:

★ **See, Hear, and Sing**

As a group, visit this America's Library feature for an introduction to some of the wonderful audio and movie files in the American Memory collection. Check out these music related highlights!

http://www.americaslibrary.gov/cgi-bin/page.cgi/sh

Jammin Jukebox: Click on the Jammin Jukebox icon to hear historical audio files, view cool movies, and read fun facts.

Introduce a unit on World War I with George M. Cohan's song, "Over There."

Sousa's "Stars and Stripes Forever" March, played by the Imperial Marimba Band, will start toes tapping and hands clapping!

Children's Songs: Listen to favorite children's songs and games of the past including "Big-Foot Rena," "Mary Mack," and "Who Do You Love?"

Are any of the old songs familiar to students?

Uncommon Instruments: Have you heard of a misnice? Or a zurna? Or a cimbalom? Tune in here to listen to sounds and learn about early musical instruments.

★ ***American Variety Stage Sampler***

Give each student a copy of the activity page.

Students can play the recordings they found and share their answers with the class.

★ ***Sousa Search***

Give each student a copy of the activity page.

Play recordings of Sousa marches while students search for pictures, sound files, and historic sheet music related to Sousa's life. Sites are listed below.

1. http://memory.loc.gov/cgi-bin/query/r?ammem/pan:@field (NUMBER+@band(pan+6a27273))

2. http://memory.loc.gov/cgi-bin/query/r?ammem/hawp:@field(NUMBER+@band (codhawp+00105161))

3. http://memory.loc.gov/cgi-bin/query/r?ammem/bbpix:@field (NUMBER+@band(cph+3g0-3222))

4. http://memory.loc.gov/cgi-bin/query/r?ammem/papr:@field (NUMBER+@band(edrs+50688r))

5. http://memory.loc.gov/cgi-bin/query/r?ammem/flwpabib:@field (DOCID+@lit(3381a6))

Extend this activity by having students locate biographical information and listen to more of Sousa's music by visiting the John Philip Sousa site maintained by the Dallas Wind Symphony.

http://www.dws.org/sousa/

Name _____ Date _____

American Variety Stage Sampler

Did you know that songs, sounds, and speeches were once recorded on wax cylinders and played on machines people cranked by hand? Our technology has changed quite a bit since the late 19th century!

1. Go to the *American Variety Stage Collection*.

http://memory.loc.gov/ammem/vshtml/vshome.html

2. Click on *Sound Recordings.*

3. Select "Browse Title List." Sample five or more of the recordings from the collection.

4. Select the one you like best and download it for later playback.

Title: _____

Performer: _____

Date recorded: _____

5. Listen to the recording carefully several times. Then answer the questions.

Did you think the recording was entertaining? _____

Why or why not? _____

_____

_____

What did this recording indicate about the time when it was produced?

_____

_____

What kind of audience might have enjoyed this recording?

_____

How do you think today's listeners would feel about the recording? _____

_____

_____

_____

Sousa Search

John Philip Sousa (1854–1932) was America's most famous composer of marches.

To begin this scavenger hunt, go to the *American Memory* search page.

http://memory.loc.gov/ammem/mdbquery.html

1. Locate a panoramic photograph featuring Sousa.

Where is Chautauqua located? _____

Why was Sousa at Chautauqua? _____

2. Locate a photograph in which Sousa is pictured with William (Buffalo Bill) Cody.

When was the photo taken? _____

Where was the photo taken? _____

Why were the people gathered together? _____

3. Locate sheet music picturing John Philip Sousa with his baseball team.

What is the title of the song? _____

Who wrote the song? _____

4. Locate a recording of Sousa's arrangement of the "U.S. Field Artillery March."

What is another name for this song? _____

Who wrote the song? _____

What band recorded the song? _____

5. Locate a recording of the "Stars and Stripes Forever" played on a bazooka. Listen to the recording.

What is a bazooka? _____

Where was this song recorded? _____

Who was the performer? _____

Celebrate America's Symbols

Students locate, examine, and research American Memory documents portraying American symbols.

Celebrate America with Symbols from American Memory
http://memory.loc.gov/ammem/ndlpedu/educators/newsletter/november01/tik_4.html

A More Perfect Union: Symbolizing the National Union of States
http://www.loc.gov/exhibits/us.capitol/s1.html

Activities:

★ *Discover America's Earliest Symbols*

Give each student a copy of the activity page and the Primary Resource Companion.

Have students prepare oral presentations of the information they find.

★ *Celebrate America with Patriotic Symbols*

Divide the class into groups of 3 to 5 students.

Give each group a copy of the activity page.

Give each student a copy of the "Celebrate America Worksheet: Symbols of America." Available online at:

http://memory.loc.gov/ammem/ndlpedu/community/am_newsletter/november01/tik_4ws.html

Symbols can be glued to red, white, and blue construction paper to make a Patriotic Symbols display for your classroom or library.

If possible, provide these reference sources for students to use:

West, Delno C. and Jean M. *Uncle Sam and Old Glory: Symbols of America*. Atheneum, 2000.

Batemen, Teresa. *Red, White, Blue and Uncle Who? The Stories behind Some of America's Patriotic Symbols*. Holiday House, 2001.

★ *Design a New American Symbol*

Brainstorm with students what America means to them today. Have them design an original symbol for America in the twenty-first century. Their product could be in the form of a pledge, poem, song, or visual symbol.

Have them write an explanation of the meaning of their new symbol.

Extension activity: Students can create buttons, banners, or posters featuring their symbols.

Discover America's Earliest Symbols

16.1

1. Go to *A More Perfect Union* to find links to images of the snake, eagle, Great Seal, Minerva, and other early American symbols.

http://www.loc.gov/exhibits/us.capitol/s1.html

2. Read the explanatory text at the beginning of the exhibit.

Print out a copy of one document in the collection.

3. Examine the document and complete the Primary Resource Organizer page.

4. Use other reference materials to research the symbols in the document.

5. Write a paragraph that answers these questions.

Who first used this symbol to represent the union?

What does the symbol look like?

When did the symbol first appear in connection with American history?

Where was the symbol published?

Why was this symbol chosen to represent the political views of the times?

How does this symbol compare to ones we use today?

Celebrate America with Patriotic Symbols

As a group:

Discuss each question. Have one member write the group's answers.

1. What are patriotic symbols?

_____

_____

2. What do patriotic symbols mean to Americans?

_____

_____

3. What do patriotic symbols indicate to visitors from other countries?

_____

_____

4. List 10 well-known American patriotic symbols.

_____

_____

_____

_____

_____

5. Search the American Memory collection for examples of patriotic symbols. If you find some not listed above, add them to your list.

On your own:

6. Print a patriotic symbol and information about that symbol.

7. Complete the Celebrate America Worksheet.

Women in American Memory

Turn-of-the-Century First Ladies...
Who's that Lady???

Who's that Lady?

Home | Teacher Page | Student Page | Resources | Answer Page

36.2

Students explore American Memory documents related to women's history.

By Popular Demand: "Votes for Women" Suffrage Pictures, 1850–1920
This selection of 38 documents offers visual views of the suffrage movement.

http://memory.loc.gov/ammem/vfwhtml/vfwhome.html

Votes for Women: Selections from the National American Woman Suffrage Association Collection, 1848–1921
This collection contains books, pamphlets, and other artifacts documenting the suffrage campaign.

http://memory.loc.gov/ammem/naw/nawshome.html

One Hundred Years toward Suffrage: An Overview
This timeline outlines the main events of the suffrage movement from 1776 through 1923.

http://memory.loc.gov/ammem/naw/nawstime.html

The Struggle for Women's Suffrage: Selected Images from the Collections of the Library of Congress
This site is a Prints and Photographs reference aid.

http://lcweb.loc.gov/rr/print/076_vfw.html

Activities:

★ *Visual Timeline of Women's Suffrage: 1820–1920*

Assign different years or periods between 1820 and 1920 to each student.

Give each student a copy of the activity page.

Have students rewrite their terrific trivia facts on 3" x 5" index cards and combine them with the other material they found chronologically to create a timeline of documents and photographs showing highlights of 100 years (1820–1920) of the Women's Suffrage Movement in the United States.

They can create a visual timeline display in a hallway or compile material to make a class book.

Option: Have students combine their material to create group collages.

★ *Who's That Lady?*

As a group, help students explore the American Memory collection and other resources to locate answers to challenge questions about four famous turn-of-the-century American first ladies: Frances Folsom Cleveland, Ida Saxton McKinley, Edith Kermit Carow Roosevelt, and Helen Herron Taft.

http://memory.loc.gov/ammem/ndlpedu/features/lady/index.html

Teacher implementation tips located on the "Teacher Page" provide basic, challenging, and bonus questions. Informational resource links can be found on the "Resources" page.

★ *Women Pioneers in American Memory*

In this online feature, students explore sources related to women who sought to make better lives for themselves, their families, and society.

Divide students into four groups to study the four major sections in this featured site: Westward, Suffrage, Struggle for Equality, and On the Job.

http://memory.loc.gov/ammem/ndlpedu/features/women/women.html

Have them find information that addresses these broad questions:

What was life like for women during that time period in America?

What types of social issues did women face?

What did women do to effect change?

Have each group present an oral summary to the class, using documents to illustrate what they discovered.

Students could use links to photographs, journals, letters, sound recordings, and movie files to enhance their presentations.

As a class, complete the Women Today section of the feature. Discuss issues that concern women today.

Women's Suffrage: 1820–1920

1. Use the sites listed to find documents, photos, and terrific trivia about the Women's Suffrage movement in the U.S.

2. For each year or time period assigned, find and print three to five documents, images, or other primary sources related to the Women's Suffrage movement in the U.S.

3. Label each item with the year. Add a short statement about its significance to the Women's Suffrage movement.

Suggested sites to search:

By Popular Demand: "Votes for Women" Suffrage Pictures, 1850–1920

http://memory.loc.gov/ammem/vfwhtml/vfwhome.html

Votes for Women: Selections from the National American Woman Suffrage Association Collection, 1848–1921

http://memory.loc.gov/ammem/naw/nawshome.html

One Hundred Years toward Suffrage: An Overview

http://memory.loc.gov/ammem/naw/nawstime.html

The Struggle for Women's Suffrage: Selected Images from the Collections of the Library of Congress

http://lcweb.loc.gov/rr/print/076_vfw.html

4. Find three interesting bits of terrific trivia related to the Women's Suffrage movement for any year between 1820 and 1920. Include the date for each trivia item.

Date

_____   _____
          _____
          _____
          _____
          _____
_____   _____
          _____
          _____
          _____
_____   _____
          _____
          _____
          _____

Photo Credits

(All photos courtesy of the Library of Congress unless otherwise noted.)

page 1 Stereoview of the Library of Congress. Underwood and Underwood, 2002 (from the collection of Gail Petri)

page 2 American Memory Collection Finder Page (screen shot)

http://memory.loc.gov/ammem/collections/finder.html

page 3 "Voices for Votes: The Struggle for Suffrage"—online lesson by Gail Petri and Doris Waud (Learning Page lesson graphic)

http://memory.loc.gov/ammem/ndlpedu/lessons/00/suffrage/index.html

page 4 Celebrate American Memory Hall Display (photo by Gail Petri)

page 9 "Primary Source Toolkit" (Learning Page graphic)

http://memory.loc.gov/ammem/ndlpedu/educators/workshop/discover/toolkit.html

page 11 American Memory Historical Collections (Homepage graphic)

http://memory.loc.gov/ammem/

page 13 Emergence of Advertising in America (Homepage graphic)

http://memory.loc.gov/ammem/award98/ncdhtml/eaahome.html

page 15 Words and Deeds in America (Homepage graphic)

http://memory.loc.gov/ammem/mcchtml/corhome.html

page 15 "Civil War photograph album, ca. 1861–65; Carte 71—Samuel Sprigg Carroll" from the Words and Deeds in American History Collection

http://memory.loc.gov/cgibin/query/r?ammem/mcccartes:@field(DOCID+@lit(mcccartes/023071f))

page 16 "Civil War photograph album, ca. 1861–65; Carte 1—Abraham Lincoln" from the Words and Deeds in American History Collection

http://memory.loc.gov/cgibin/query/r?ammem/mcccartes:@field(DOCID+@lit(mcccartes/006001f))

page 18 Edward C. Curtis's North American Indian (Homepage graphic)

http://memory.loc.gov/ammem/award98/ienhtml/curthome.html

page 18 American Indians of the Pacific Northwest (Homepage graphic)

http://memory.loc.gov/ammem/award98/wauhtml/aipnhome.html

page 20 "Walpi snake priest" (The North American Indian; v.12); Northwestern University Library, Edward S. Curtis's 'The North American Indian': the Photographic Images, 2001.

http://memory.loc.gov/award/iencurt/cp12/cp12030v.jpg

page 20 "Nez Perce babe" (The North American Indian; v.08); Northwestern University Library, Edward S. Curtis's 'The North American Indian': the Photographic Images, 2001.

http://memory.loc.gov/award/iencurt/cp08/cp08011v.jpg

page 21 American Girl Dolls holding sign (photo by Gail Petri)

page 27 America's Story from America's Library graphic

http://www.americaslibrary.gov/cgi-bin/page.cgi

page 30 "Washington's Personal copy of the Declaration of Independence" from the Library of Congress Manuscript Division (Top Treasures of the Library of Congress exhibit)

http://www.loc.gov/exhibits/treasures/tr00.html

page 31 "First Draft of the Gettysburg Address" from the Library of Congress Manuscript Division (Top Treasures of the Library of Congress exhibit)

http://www.loc.gov/exhibits/treasures/trt034.html

page 32 Origins of American Animation (Homepage graphic)

http://memory.loc.gov/ammem/oahtml/oahome.html

page 33 "Humorous phases of funny faces/Vitagraph; producer and animator, J. Stuart Blackton" from the Origins of American Animation Collection

http://hdl.loc.gov/loc.mbrsmi/animp.4064

page 34 Historical fiction books (photo by Gail Petri)

page 35 Selected Civil War Photographs (Homepage graphic)

http://memory.loc.gov/ammem/cwphtml/cwphome.html

page 35 California As I Saw It (Homepage graphic)

http://memory.loc.gov/ammem/cbhtml/cbhome.html

page 36 The Northern Great Plains, 1880–1920 (Homepage graphic)

http://memory.loc.gov/ammem/award97/ndfahtml/ngphome.html

page 36 By Popular Demand: "Votes for Women" Suffrage Pictures, 1850–1920 (Homepage graphic)

http://memory.loc.gov/ammem/vfwhtml/vfwhome.html

Photo Credits

page 36 "Suffering Under a Great Injustice"—Ansel Adams' Photographs of Japanese-American Internment at Manzanar (Homepage graphic)

http://memory.loc.gov/ammem/aamhtml/aamhome.html

page 37 Built in America: Historic American Buildings Survey (HABS) and the Historic American Engineering Record (HAER) (Homepage graphic)

http://memory.loc.gov/ammem/hhhtml/hhhome.html

page 38 "Golden Gate Bridge, San Francisco, California" from the Built in America: Historic American Buildings Survey (HABS) and the Historic American Engineering Record (HAER) Collection

http://memory.loc.gov/ammem/hhhtml/cahh.html

page 38 "Beebe Windmill, Bridgehampton, New York" from the Built in America: Historic American Buildings Survey (HABS) and the Historic American Engineering Record (HAER) Collection

http://memory.loc.gov/ammem/hhhtml/ny1hh.html

page 39 America's Story—Jump Back in Time (logo)

http://www.americaslibrary.gov/cgi-bin/page.cgi/jb

page 39 American Memory Timeline (Learning Page feature graphic)

http://memory.loc.gov/ammem/ndlpedu/features/timeline/index.html

page 41 America's Story—Jump Back in Time—Pick a Date to Visit (logo)

http://www.americaslibrary.gov/cgi-bin/page.cgi/jb

page 43 Touring Turn-of-the-Century America—Photographs from the Detroit Publishing Company 1880–1920 (Homepage graphic)

http://memory.loc.gov/ammem/detroit/dethome.html

page 43 History of the American West 1860–1920 (Homepage graphic)

http://memory.loc.gov/ammem/award97/codhtml/hawphome.html

page 46 America at Work, America at Leisure: Motion Pictures from 1894–1915 (Homepage graphic)

http://memory.loc.gov/ammem/awlhtml/awlhome.html

page 48 "Occupational portrait of a woman working at a sewing machine" from the America's First Look into the Camera: Daguerreotype Portraits and Views, 1839–1864 Collection

http://memory.loc.gov/cgi-bin/query/r?ammem/dag:@field(NUMBER+@band(cph+3c06400))

Photo Credits

page 48 "Occupational portrait of an unidentified stonecutter" from the America's First Look into the Camera: Daguerrreotype Portraits and Views, 1839–1864 Collection

http://memory.loc.gov/cgi-bin/query/r?ammem/dag:@field(NUMBER+@band(cph+3d02040))

page 50 "Election Day" from the By Popular Demand: "Votes for Women" Suffrage Pictures, 1850–1920 Collection

http://memory.loc.gov/cgi-bin/query/r?ammem/suffrg:@field(NUMBER+@band(cph+3a51845))

page 50 "Our destiny is in his hands" from An American Time Capsule: Three Centuries of Broadsides and Other Printed Ephemera Collection

http://hdl.loc.gov/loc.rbc/rbpe.0840270e

page 52 "Boy sweeper, wearing knickers, standing alongside carding machine in Lincoln Cotton Mills, Evansville, Indiana. Lewis Hine, photographer." Photographic print. 1908 Oct. from the Library of Congress, Prints and Photographs Division, National Child Labor Committee Collection

http://lcweb.loc.gov/rr/print/coll/207-b.html

page 54 "Shrimp and Oyster Worker, Biloxi, Miss. Lewis Hine, photographer. 1911 Feb." from the Library of Congress, Prints and Photographs Division, National Child Labor Committee Collection

http://lcweb.loc.gov/rr/print/coll/207-b.html

page 55 Civil War Treasures from the New York Historical Society (Homepage graphic)

http://memory.loc.gov/ammem/ndlpcoop/nhihtml/cwnyhshome.html

page 55 Selected Civil War Photographs (Homepage graphic)

http://memory.loc.gov/ammem/cwphtml/cwphome.html

page 57 "Gettysburg, Pa. Alfred R. Waud, artist of Harper's Weekly, sketching on battlefield" from the Selected Civil War Photographs

http://memory.loc.gov/cgi-bin/query/r?ammem/cwar:@field(NUMBER+@band(cwp+4a39436))

page 60 America's First Look into the Camera: Daguerreotype Portraits and Views, 1839–1864 (homepage graphic)

http://memory.loc.gov/ammem/daghtml/daghome.html

page 61 "Unidentified group in costume with John Barrett, Director General of the Pan American Union" from the Taking the Long View: Panoramic Photographs 1851–1991 Collection

http://memory.loc.gov/cgi-bin/query/r?ammem/pan:@field(NUMBER+@band(cph+3c30865))

Photo Credits

page 62 "Making purchase at traveling grocery store, Forrest City, Arkansas" from the America from the Great Depression to World War II: Photographs from the FSA-OWI, 1935–1945 Collection

http://memory.loc.gov/cgi-bin/query/r?ammem/fsaall:@field(NUMBER+@band(fsa+8a23574))

page 64 "Mount Vernon dining & oyster saloon ... The subscriber respectfully informs his friends and the public that he has fitted in the above place with every convenience, for a first-class restaurant ... James Patterson ... Boston, June, 1859" from An American Time Capsule: Three Centuries of Broadsides and Other Printed Ephemera Collection.

http://hdl.loc.gov/loc.rbc/rbpe.06403100

page 67 "How to conserve household gas. There's a time for everything, and the time to read a cookbook is before you light the gas, not after" from the America from the Great Depression to World War II: Photographs from the FSA-OWI, 1935–1945

http://memory.loc.gov/cgi-bin/query/r?ammem/fsaall:@filreq(@field(NUMBER+@band(fsa+8b04687))+@field(COLLID+fsa))

pages 69 and 71 "Thomas Jefferson's drawing of a macaroni machine and instructions for making pasta, ca. 1787" from the Words and Deeds in American History Collection

http://memory.loc.gov/cgi-bin/query/r?ammem/mcc:@field(DOCID+@lit(mcc/027))

pages 69 and 71 "Letter with illustrated fable, Theodore Roosevelt to Theodore Roosevelt, Jr., 11 July 1890" from the Words and Deeds in American History Collection

http://memory.loc.gov/cgi-bin/query/r?ammem/mcc:@field(DOCID+@lit(mcc/045))

page 73 "Campaign ribbon. [n. p.] [c. 1844]" from An American Time Capsule: Three Centuries of Broadsides and Other Printed Ephemera Collection

http://hdl.loc.gov/loc.rbc/rbpe.1190280a

pages 73 and 76 "The first gymnacyclidium for ladies and gentlemen" from An American Time Capsule: Three Centuries of Broadsides and Other Printed Ephemera Collection

http://hdl.loc.gov/loc.rbc/rbpe.34101800

page 78 Creative American Portraits by Carl Van Vechten 1932–1964 (Homepage graphic)

http://memory.loc.gov/ammem/vvhtml/vvhome.html

page 80 "Anthony, Susan Brownell" from the Prints and Photographs Division

http://lcweb.loc.gov/rr/print/235_poa.html#AnthonyS

Photo Credits

page 81 American Variety Stage: Vaudeville and Popular Entertainment 1870–1920 (Houdini graphic)

http://memory.loc.gov/ammem/vshtml/vshdini.html

page 84 "The Big Picture" (Learning Page activity graphic)

http://memory.loc.gov/ammem/ndlpedu/features/puzzle/puzintro.html

page 84 "Three men seated at table with checkerboards, spectators looking on" from the Voices from the Dust Bowl: The Charles L. Todd and Robert Sonkin Miugrant Worker Collection, 1940–1941 Collection

http://memory.loc.gov/cgi-bin/query/r?ammem/toddbib:@field(DOCID+@lit(p019))

page 85 "Inaugurations—I Spy—Lincoln's Inauguration" (Learning Page activity graphic)

http://memory.loc.gov/ammem/ndlpedu/features/inaug/ispy2.html

page 86 "Unidentified group in costume with John Barrett, Director General of the Pan American Union" from the Taking the Long View: Panoramic Photographs 1851–1991 Collection

http://memory.loc.gov/cgi-bin/query/r?ammem/pan:@field(NUMBER+@band(cph+3c30865))

page 86 Snow photo collage (photo by Gail Petri)

page 88 Tombstone Tales writing activity (photo by Gail Petri)

pages 92 and 95 "Italian immigrant family at Ellis Island" from the Prints and Photographs Division, Reproduction Number LC-USZ62-67910.

page 92 "Head of Statue of Liberty on display in park in Paris" from the Prints and Photographs Division, Reproduction Number LC-USZ62-18086

pages 96 and 100 "Detail of map: The City of Washington Birds-Eye view from the Potomac-looking North" from Map Collections: 1500–Present

http://hdl.loc.gov/loc.gmd/g3851a.pm001073

page 103 I spy numbers in American Memory (photo by Gail Petri)

page 105 I spy numbers in America Memory sample questions (photo by Gail Petri)

page 108 "Emigrants (i.e., immigrants) landing at Ellis Island" from the Inventing Entertainment: The Motion Pictures and Sound Recordings of the Edison Companies Collection

http://hdl.loc.gov/loc.mbrsmi/lcmp002.m2a10987

Photo Credits

page 110 Student created photo postcards (photo by Gail Petri)

page 117 Poetry 180 (Library of Congress logo)

http://www.loc.gov/poetry/180/

page 118 "8 lines of poetry advertising Mahlon Day's juvenile book store" from An American Time Capsule: Three Centuries of Broadsides and Other Printed Ephemera Collection

http://hdl.loc.gov/loc.rbc/rbpe.13002200

page 119 Poet at Work: Recovered Notebooks from the Thomas Biggs Harned Walt Whitman Collection (Homepage graphic)

http://memory.loc.gov/ammem/wwhtml/wwhome.html

page 122 By Popular Demand: Portrait of the Presidents and First Ladies (Homepage graphic)

http://memory.loc.gov/ammem/odmdhtml/preshome.html

page 123 "I Do Solemnly Swear." Presidential Inaugurations (Homepage graphic)

http://memory.loc.gov/ammem/pihtml/pihome.html

page 123 Wall of Presidents photo collage (photo by Gail Petri)

page 128 American Environmental Photographs, 1891–1936 (Homepage graphic)

http://memory.loc.gov/ammem/award97/icuhtml/aephome.html

page 134 American Variety Stage: Vaudeville and Popular Entertainment 1870–1920—Sound Recordings (Homepage graphic)

http://memory.loc.gov/ammem/vshtml/vssound.html

page 138 Celebrate American Memory Hall Display (photo by Gail Petri)

page 138 "Benjamin Franklin 'Join or Die' Pennsylvania Gazette (Philadelphia), May 9, 1754" from the Temple of Liberty; Building the Capitol for a New Nation exhibit

http://lcweb.loc.gov/exhibits/us.capitol/one.jpg

page 140 "First Publication of Great Seal" from the Temple of Liberty; Building the Capitol for a New Nation exhibit

page 142 "Who's That Lady?" (Learning Page feature graphic)

http://memory.loc.gov/ammem/vfwhtml/vfwhome.html

Index